The Pioneer Woman

By the American sculptor BRYANT BAKER.
The statue is in Ponca City, Oklahoma

The World of Music

BLENDING VOICES

By

MABELLE GLENN

DIRECTOR OF MUSIC, PUBLIC SCHOOLS, KANSAS CITY, MISSOURI

HELEN S. LEAVITT

INSTRUCTOR IN MUSIC, BOSTON UNIVERSITY AND THE WHEELOCK SCHOOL
BOSTON, MASSACHUSETTS

VICTOR L. F. REBMANN

FORMERLY DIRECTOR OF MUSIC, WESTCHESTER COUNTY, NEW YORK

EARL L. BAKER

FORMERLY DIRECTOR OF PUBLIC SCHOOL MUSIC DEPARTMENT
LAWRENCE COLLEGE, APPLETON, WISCONSIN

ART EDITOR

C. VALENTINE KIRBY

STATE DIRECTOR OF ART EDUCATION, PENNSYLVANIA

GINN AND COMPANY

BOSTON · NEW YORK · CHICAGO · LONDON · ATLANTA · DALLAS · COLUMBUS · SAN FRANCISCO

The World of Music

KINDERGARTEN

SING A SONG
PLAY A TUNE

ELEMENTARY GRADES

LISTEN AND SING
TUNING UP
RHYTHMS AND RIMES
SONGS OF MANY LANDS
BLENDING VOICES
TUNES AND HARMONIES

ALL GRADES

SINGING DAYS

Classified Contents

6   **Classified Contents**

There are here 126 folk songs and 56 composed songs.

Rote Experience: 22 songs, indicated by the word ROTE under the title.

Music Reading: 160 songs; review of known elements; two-part singing continued; introduction of 6/8 measure and dotted eighth and sixteenth notes.

All the songs correlate with the child's studies, interests, and experience.

Reproductions of Noted Pictures: The Pioneer Woman, *Bryant Baker*, frontispiece; The Roving Cowboy, *William M. Berger*, p. 19; Fairy Tales, *James J. Shannon*, p. 38; The Primitive Sculptor, *E. I. Couse*, p. 55; Lincoln, *Augustus St. Gaudens*, p. 106; Heavy Load, *E. Kaempffer*, p. 123; Herd in the Sunlight, *Émile Claus*, p. 142; The Shepherdess, *Henry Lerolle*, p. 159.

BLENDING VOICES

Music Everywhere

ROTE

Carol Fuller

Frances McCollin

1. Mu - sic can be heard ev-'ry-where, Chords that sun-beams
2. Mu - sic can be heard ev-'ry-where, Call - ing those who

write on the air; Where flow - ers grow, their bells are
know it is there. Ech - oes of light the moon is

ring - ing, Wind plays a tune to branch - es
bring - ing, Notes from a harp that night is

swing - ing; High in the sky the hap - py
string - ing; No voice is near, yet mu - sic

birds that fly Set all the world to sing - ing.
I can hear, Be - cause my heart is sing - ing.

Nanina

English version by
Christine Turner Curtis

Italian Folk Song

Grazioso
mf

1. Sun-light is fall-ing in the square, Na - ni - na. The
2. Fas - ten a rose-bud in your hair, Na - ni - na! In

domes are gleam - ing, the foun - tains stream - ing.
ol - ives old - en, the buds are gold - en.

Gui - do[1] is play-ing on his con - cer - ti - na; The
Gui - do is play-ing on his con - cer - ti - na; We'll

doves are fly - ing on pink and sil - ver plumes.
dream to - geth - er where sweet a - ca - cia blooms.

The Elf

Rose Fyleman

Anna von W. Grille

Leggiero
mp
cres.

1. On an ear - ly, dew - y, pearl - y, sun - ny
2. Was he on - ly feel-ing lone - ly As a -

[1]Pronounced "gwē'dō."

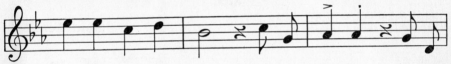

morn-ing of the spring, Went an elf - kin by his
cross the fields he went? Lit - tle elf - kin by his

self - kin Through the mead-ows on his way, ho! And I
self - kin, Though he seemed so blithe and gay, ho! 'Twas a

pon-dered, as I wan-dered, On the song I heard him
pret - ty lit-tle dit - ty, But I know not what it

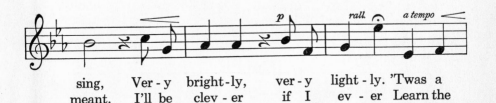

sing, Ver - y bright-ly, ver - y light - ly. 'Twas a
meant. I'll be clev - er if I ev - er Learn the

hen - ny and a hon - ey and a heigh - ho!
mean-ing of his hen - ny hon - ey heigh - ho!

The Weary Spinner

Adapted from the original by
Frances Ford

Scotch Folk Song

1. Sheep   and   cat - tle   have   I   none,   O!
2. Far   he   sails   the   deep   blue   o - cean;
3. Wea - ry   spin - ning,   wea - ry   wait - ing,

Barns and hous - es   nev-er   a   one, O! Turns my spin - dle
Where he goes I've   nev-er   a   no - tion. Strong and true is
Wea - ry hands the   rush-es are plait-ing; Toil will nev - er

in   the   sun, O!   Till   my   lad comes   home   a - gain.
my de - vo - tion   Till   my   lad comes   home   a - gain.
be   a - bat - ing   Till   my   lad comes   home   a - gain.

Songs of Gold

Louise Ayres Garnett

Russian Folk Tune

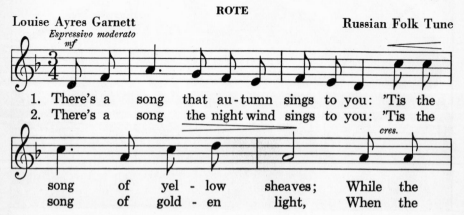

1. There's a   song   that au - tumn   sings   to you: 'Tis the
2. There's a   song   the night wind sings   to you: 'Tis the

song   of   yel - low   sheaves;   While   the
song   of   gold - en   light,   When   the

earth   is   rest - ing   dream - i - ly   'Neath the
har - vest moon has   o - pened wide   All   her

tap - es - try of   leaves. Oh, the   song   that au - tumn
pet - als to the   night. Oh, the   song   the night wind

sings to you   Is   a   song   of yel - low   sheaves.
sings to you   Is   a   song   of gold - en   light.

The Secret

ROTE

Jane Beecham   Margaret K. Fowler

1. I have a hid - den treas - ure I
heard it just this morn - ing, I've

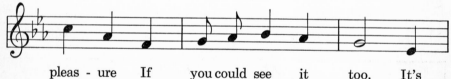

can - not show to you. 'Twould dou - ble all the
kept it safe all day Be - cause I had a

pleas - ure If you could see it too. It's
warn - ing I can - not dis - o - bey. I'm

not what pi - rates gath - er, Or what you dig to
sure you could - n't guess it, But you would like it

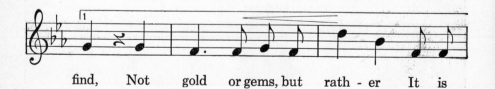

find, Not gold or gems, but rath - er It is

The Secret (*Continued*)

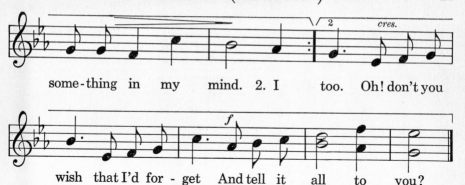

some-thing in my mind. 2. I too. Oh! don't you

wish that I'd for - get And tell it all to you?

Indian Call

ROTE

Luther Wilde

Winnebago Indian Melody

Dolce cantabile

1. A - way through the fern and the deep for - est
2. When night hangs her stars in the dark wood - land

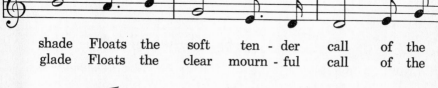

shade Floats the soft ten - der call of the
glade Floats the clear mourn - ful call of the

dove, Coo, · · come a - way, In - dian maid.
owl, Hoo, · · come a - way, In - dian maid.

16

Early One Morning

Paraphrase by
Marjorie Knapp

English Folk Song

English version by
Christine Turner Curtis

Danish Folk Song

1. All the birds are gath - 'ring, Wheel - ing and
2. Un - der oaks and ma - ples Troop we to -

turn - ing: Soon they flock to sum - mer lands Where
geth - er; There to hunt for brush and twig To

south-ern suns are burn - ing. Pur - ple hang the
warm the frost - y weath - er. Karl shall climb the

beech - es, Crim - son sets the ear - ly sun.
fir tree, Chris - tian gath - er cones to burn.

Slow creep the cat - tle home - ward;
See, how the tim - id rab - bits

Fog - gy days are soon be - gun.
Scur - ry home - ward through the fern!

The Roving Cowboy

Paraphrase from "Singing Cowboy"   From "Singing Cowboy"

1. Oh, I'm a rov - ing cow - boy From
2. Oh, come, you rov - ing cow - boys! You

off the West - ern plains; My trade is strap-ping
see I'm bound to roam. I'm leav - ing my dear

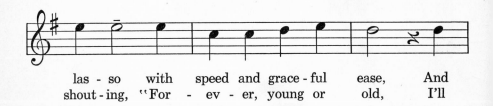

sad - dles And pull-ing bri - dle reins. I can throw a
moth - er, Two sis-ters, and a home. Hear me, boys, a -

las - so with speed and grace - ful ease, And
shout - ing, "For - ev - er, young or old, I'll

I can rope a bron - co, And ride him where I please.
fol-low long-horned cat - tle: A life that's free and bold."

Ginn and Company

The Roving Cowboy

From a painting by the American artist WILLIAM M. BERGER

Spinning Song

English version by
Rose Fyleman

Swedish Folk Song

Andante cantabile
mp

1. Close and close the shad - ows steal;
2. Win - ter weath - er will not stay.

Night will soon be com - ing. Turn, my lit - tle
When the spring's be - gin - ning, I shall put my

spin - ning wheel! I love your gen - tle hum - ming.
wheel a - way, Shall put a - way my spin - ning.

mf

Round and round you light - ly go,
I shall wear a gown of red,

mp

Gleam - ing by the chim - ney's glow,
Wo - ven of the wool - en thread

rall. e dim.

Hum - ming, hum - ming, hum - ming.
That my wheel is spin - ning.

Annette Wynne

Swiss Folk Tune

1. Day is go - ing like a rose;
2. Day is go - ing like a rose;

Qui - et sleep at - tend thee. Now the dew - y
God's arm is a - round us. God's love on His

eye - lids close; An - gels will de - fend thee.
chil - dren flows When the shades sur - round us.

Blow Fast

ROTE

Adapted from the original by
Christine Turner Curtis

Scotch Folk Song

Con grazia
mf

1. I sailed my ship in - to Tor - ri - don Bay;
2. She smiled and tum - bled my wits in a whirl;
3. I drove my ves - sel through hail and through rain;
4. I rode him pranc - ing up Tor - ri - don Hill;

I left her a - float at the moor - ing; And
Her eyes spar - kled round - er and bright - er; In
The wind in the hal - yards was whin - ing; I
I gal - loped him o - ver the riv - er. Her

there up - on the high - land way I met a lass al -
truth her neck was like a pearl, Nor could a swan be
brought her home a gold - en chain Of pearl and ru - by
moth - er met me on the sill. A - lack, she's gone for -

lur - ing. We walked by mead-ow-land, riv - er, and bay, She
whit - er. "I'll wed you, tru - ly, my sail - or, my Dirk." Her
twin - ing. I sailed my ves - sel to is - lands un-told, Be -
ev - er! Blow fast, oh rip - ple! Blow free - ly, oh foam! 'Tis

tripped it as light as a feath - er; Her head was tossed; her
eyes twin-kled pur-ple and larg - er. "But I must hie me
neath me the bil-lows were slid - ing; With milk-white charg - er
o - cean and sail - or to - geth - er; For I shall nev - er

laugh was gay; She danced a - cross the heath - er.
to the kirk Up - on a milk - white charg - er."
in the hold, To port my ship came rid - ing.
more come home To walk the pur - ple heath - er.

In Riga

Marjorie Knapp

Lettish Folk Tune

Allegretto
mf

1. Here are path - ways, nar - row, wind - ing;
2. Here are parks a - blaze with blos - soms;

Here are oak trees grow - ing.
Here a riv - er flow - ing.

Books

Louise Ayres Garnett

Polish Folk Tune

1. My best ad - ven - tures come on print - ed pag - es;
2. When it is storm - y, get the horse to speed - ing;

Words swift - ly mov - ing take me through the ag - es.
Ride him through chap - ters, let him do the lead - ing.

No horse can beat me, noth - ing can de - feat me;
Thun - der can clat - ter, dust the wind can scat - ter.

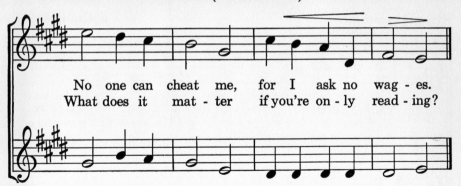

No one can cheat me, for I ask no wag - es.
What does it mat - ter if you're on - ly read - ing?

Nuts and Apples

Mary Smith

English Folk Tune

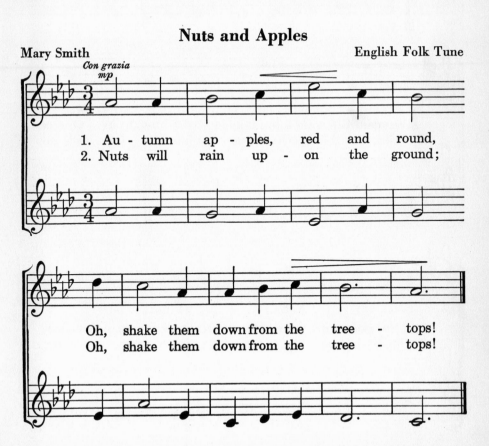

Con grazia
mp

1. Au - tumn ap - ples, red and round,
2. Nuts will rain up - on the ground;

Oh, shake them down from the tree - tops!
Oh, shake them down from the tree - tops!

To a Pigeon in Venice

Rose Fyleman

Italian Folk Tune

Dolce espressivo
mp

1. Gen - tle and grace-ful and pret - ty As your
2. Yours are the sun - ny bright spac - es And the

coun - try's beau - ti - ful daugh - ters,
bright sky glow - ing a - bove you;

Fly - ing a - bout the cit - y, O - ver its
Stran-gers from dis - tant plac - es Feed you and

cres.

shin - ing wa - ters: Nich - es of mar - ble to
praise and love you. Yours all the del - i - cate

nest in, And a per - fumed bow - er to
glo - ry Of these stones so fa - mous in

mf

rest in, Free as the soft blue air you cleave,
sto - ry; Beau-ty and sun-shine ev - 'ry - where!

Life must be fair, me - seems,   · In your love - ly
Life must be fair, me - seems,   · In your love - ly

rall. e dim.   *pp*

home of dreams, In your love - ly home of dreams.
home of dreams, In your love - ly home of dreams.

Bagpipes

Susanna Myers   Austrian Tyrol Folk Tune

Animato
mf

1. In my dreams I played a tune   On my mer - ry
2. In my dreams I played so long   I woke all the
3. In my dreams they shout-ed out, "Put a - way those

bag-pipes; This was the tune,   This lit - tle tune.
neigh-bors; I liked my tune,   This lit - tle tune.
bag-pipes! Do stop that tune!   Oh, what a tune!"

bag - pipes. Hear my tune, This lit - tle tune!
neigh - bors. Hear my tune, This lit - tle tune!
bag - pipes! Stop that tune! Oh, what a tune!

Camp Fire

ROTE

Rose Fyleman

Gypsy Folk Tune

Con anima

1. By the bon-fire's rud-dy glo-ries, · Where the
2. You may share our an-cient learn-ing, · You may
3. And if trou-ble o-ver-take you · And of

dry logs crack and blaze, You shall learn our
hear our peo'-ple tell How to read the
cit-y ways you tire, You will find all

songs and sto-ries, And the se-cret gyp-sy ways. ·
bright stars' turn-ing, How to weave a gyp-sy spell. ·
care for-sake you Here, be-side our gyp-sy fire. ·

28.

Close of Day

ROTE

Marjorie Knapp

Robert Schumann

Con espressione

1. Bells are call-ing; Now all our work is · end-ed;
2. Flow'rs are sleep-ing; The birds have ceased their sing-ing;

Dark is fall-ing, The eve-ning time is here a-gain.
Shad-ows creep-ing, The sky seems dark and far a-way.

Hear us sing-ing! Come, join in · our re-frain!
Stars are gleam-ing, They guard us · till the day.

Night is bring-ing us qui-et and slum-ber.
Night is bring-ing us si-lence and slum-ber.

Night is bring-ing us qui-et and slum-ber.
Night brings dream-ing and si-lence and slum-ber.

Smile Again

English version by
Christine Turner Curtis

Welsh Folk Song

1. Smile a - gain, smile a - gain; Smile a - gain, my love - ly Jane! Dry those pearl - y dew-drops fall - ing From your sweet blue eyes. Set a

2. Smile a - gain, smile a - gain; Smile a - gain, my love - ly Jane! When we ram - bled by the foun - tain In the sun - set blush, You were

3. Smile a - gain, smile a - gain; Smile a - gain, my love - ly Jane! For the sun be - gins to spar - kle And my heart to leap When your

rain - bow in the skies! Smile a - gain, my love - ly Jane.
sing - ing like a thrush. Smile a - gain, my love - ly Jane.
ros - y dim-ples peep! Smile a - gain, my love - ly Jane.

Halloween

Hope Ann Rhodes

Yugoslavian Folk Tune

1. Jack - o' - lan - terns! puss - y cats!
2. Mov - ing shad - ows! wish - ing caps!

Fun - ny fac - es! point - ed hats! Old black witch - es!
Strange hob - gob-lins! spook - y taps! Ap - ple duck - ing!

I have seen All these things on Hal - low - een.
can - dle - light! Lots of fun on this queer night.

Pedro[1] and Cita[2]

After the original by
Louise Ayres Garnett

Inca Folk Song

Semplice
mf

1. Pe-dro sings to the strings He is gen-tly strum -
2. Ci - ta weaves loops of leaves Fra-grant and be - com -
3. Sil - ver - white is the night; Man-y lads are thrum -

p

ming; Lit-tle wild-wood things Keep on a - hum - ming.
ing; Pe-dro keeps sing - ing; Woods go on hum - ming.
ming; Pe-dro keeps sing - ing; Woods go on hum - ming.

Where the Roses

Rose Fyleman

Mexican Folk Tune

Con grazia
UNISON *mp*

1. Where the ros - es · sweet - ly clam - ber, · Where the
2. He is hand-some, · straight and slen - der · Like the

lil - ies · scent the air, · In my bod - ice · blue and
sap-lings · in the wood; · He is faith-ful, · he is

am - ber · With a rose-bud · in my hair, ·
ten - der, · He is gen - tle, · he is good. ·

[1] Pronounced "pĕ′drô." 　　[2] Pronounced "chē′ta."

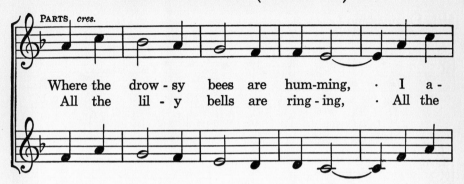

Where the drow - sy bees are hum-ming, · I a -
All the lil - y bells are ring - ing, · All the

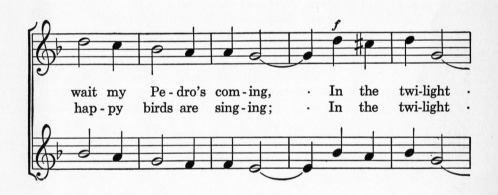

wait my Pe - dro's com - ing, · In the twi-light ·
hap - py birds are sing - ing; · In the twi-light ·

· wait his com-ing · With a rose-bud in my hair. ·
· birds are sing-ing, · "He is hon - est, he is good." ·

Portrait

Mabel Livingstone

Daniel Wolf

1. There's a pic - ture in the par - lor That was paint - ed long a - go Of a lit - tle girl with laugh - ter - lov - ing eyes. And her hair in gold - en rings 'Round her fore-head curls and clings, And her smile is like the sun in sum - mer skies. Smil - ing down through all the years From that

2. Oh, I love the fan she car - ries, And her queer old - fash - ioned clothes, And the buck - les on her shoes so quaint and small. And how bright her face ap - pears

lit - tle   o - val   frame   up - on   the   wall.

Chickadee

Lucy K. Milburn   Hungarian Folk Tune

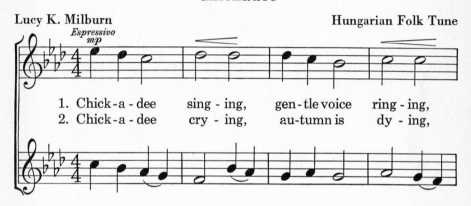

Espressivo
mp

1. Chick-a-dee   sing-ing,   gen-tle voice   ring-ing,
2. Chick-a-dee   cry-ing,   au-tumn is   dy-ing,

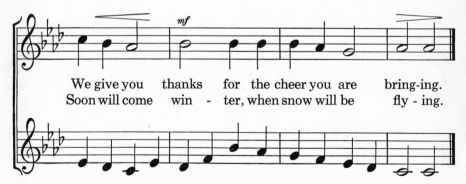

mf

We give you   thanks   for the cheer you are   bring-ing.
Soon will come   win - ter, when snow will be   fly-ing.

We give you our deep-est thanks for good cheer you are bring-ing.
Soon will come the win-ter-time, when snow-flakes will be fly-ing.

Heigh-ho! Maid of the Mill

Paraphrase by
Marjorie Knapp

Welsh Folk Song

1. Oh, come to the wood, the wood where we met!
2. A rose in my gar - den saw you go by.

Heigh - ho! Maid of the Mill. The glo - ri - ous
Heigh - ho! Maid of the Mill. She en - vied your

sun in crim - son has set. Heigh - ho!
bloom, your star - ry dark eye. Heigh - ho!

Maid of the Mill. Ac - quaint-ance in win - ter may
Maid of the Mill. The ha - zel tree rus - tled her

die with the snows, But friend-ship will blos - som as
leaves in sur - prise; She thought you a god - dess come

sweet as a rose. Oh, come to the wood, the
down from the skies. A rose in my gar - den

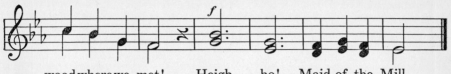

wood where we met! Heigh - ho! Maid of the Mill.
saw you go by. Heigh - ho! Maid of the Mill.

Flag Day

Clara Louise Kessler

Ukrainian Folk Tune

Maestoso

1. See the flags this morn - ing, Ev - 'ry home a -
2. Flag of our great na - tion, We of ev - 'ry

dorn - ing! Ban-ners bright, red, blue, and white, With
sta - tion Sing, "All hail! May peace pre - vail! May

sil - ver stars are gleam - ing; Through the town, both
for - tune fair at - tend thee! Ban - ner true, red,

up and down, We see the col - ors stream - ing.
white, and blue, May loy - al hearts de - fend thee!"

Fairy Tales

Painted by JAMES J. SHANNON. The picture is now
in the Metropolitan Museum of Art, New York City

Fairy Tales

Ethel Crowninshield   Bohemian-Czech Folk Tune

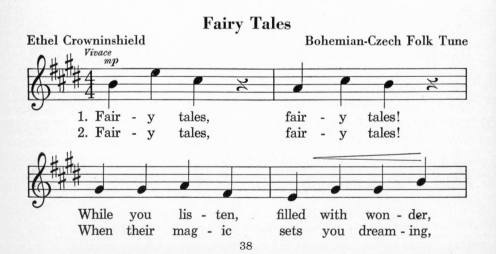

1. Fair - y   tales,   fair - y   tales!
2. Fair - y   tales,   fair - y   tales!

While   you   lis - ten,   filled   with   won - der,
When   their   mag - ic   sets   you   dream - ing,

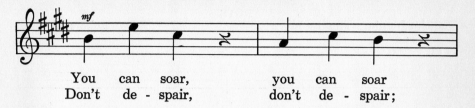

You can soar, you can soar
Don't de - spair, don't de - spair;

Back to mag - ic days of yore. See the Gold - en
Joy will take you un - a - ware. Keep your dreams and

Prin - cess walk - ing! Hear the Six Black
nev - er leave them; They'll come true if

Swans come talk - ing! Mar - vels rare, mar - vels rare
you be - lieve them. Mar - vels may, mar - vels may

Hap - pen in the ra - diant air.
Hap - pen al - most an - y day.

Camping Song

ROTE

Blanche Jennings Thompson   Robert W. Gibb

1. Ta - ra - ta - ra - ta! · Ta - ra - ta -
2. Ta - ra - ta - ra - ta! · Ta - ra - ta -
3. Ta - ra - ta - ra - ta! · Ta - ra - ta -

ra - ta! · The bu - gles call us all as
ra - ta! · Oh, ev - 'ry boy is here, no
ra - ta! · True com - rades all in line as

off we start to - geth - er. · Ta - ra - ta -
mat - ter what the weath - er. · Ta - ra - ta -
now for camp we gath - er. · Ta - ra - ta -

ra - ta! · Ta - ra - ta - ra - ta! · We'll eat to -
ra - ta! · Ta - ra - ta - ra - ta! · We'll sleep to -
ra - ta! · Ta - ra - ta - ra - ta! ·There's naught so

day in for - est gay like Rob - in Hood. ·
night be - neath the stars and find it good. ·
good as life with - in the mer - ry wood. ·

In My Garden

Rose Fyleman

Ukrainian Folk Tune

1. In my gar - den sun - ny
2. In my or - chard shad - y

The ros - es grow all white and red.
The ap - ples grow all green and red,

Sweet in sum - mer weath - er
Low a - mong the grass - es

The birds all sing to - geth - er.
The gen - tle south wind pass - es.

To my gar - den sun - ny
In my or - chard shad - y

The brown bees come for hon - ey.
There walks a gen - tle la - dy.

Sir Anton

English version by
Cecil Cowdrey

Czechoslovakian Folk Song

Con anima
mf

1. Who comes here a - rid - ing, Rid-ing far and late?
2. His fair bride a - seek - ing, He has rid-den fast;
3. To his fa-ther's cas - tle At the break of day,

'Tis Sir An-ton rid - ing To the cit - y gate.
At the cit - y por - tal Claims her now at last.
His fair bride be - side him, Soon he'll ride a - way.

f

All his knights a - sing-ing, Down the high-way swing-ing;
All his knights a - sing-ing, Down the high-way swing-ing;
Bright his ar - mor ring-ing, All his knights a - sing - ing;

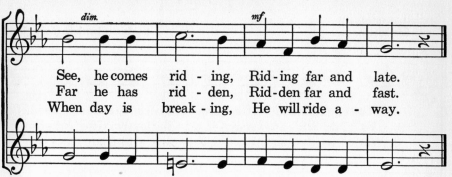

See, he comes rid - ing, Rid - ing far and late.
Far he has rid - den, Rid - den far and fast.
When day is break - ing, He will ride a - way.

Gay Young Lads

Translated by
Hannah Bailey

Lettish Folk Song

1. Gay young lads go swift - ly rid - ing, Snow-white hors - es
2. Past our farm the lads go sing - ing; I look out with
3. I would sell my sil - ver lock - et; I would emp - ty

light - ly guid - ing, O - ver rock and weed.
tear-drops spring - ing. I am sad in - deed!
purse and pock - et For a snow-white steed.

Song of the Shepherd

English version by
Margaret Widdemer

Finnish Folk Song

1. Green are the pas-tures where my sheep are feed-ing;
2. Pale in the twi-light all the lambs come trot-ting;
3. Warm in the sheep-fold they are safe from stray-ing;

Far off they wan-der till they hear my flute a-
Gray sheep and white sheep all the grass-y hill-side
Warm in my bed I dream of shep-herds' pipes a-

plead-ing, "Sheep and lambs, oh, come to your home!"
dot-ting. Sheep and lambs, oh, come to your home!
play-ing, "Sheep and lambs, oh, come to your home!"

In the English Folk Style by
Katherine K. Davis

Traditional

1. A sto - ry, a · sto - ry I'll tell you just now; It's
2. Says lit - tle Tom Dick-er, "Pray what do you mean" By
3. Then come - eth the tan - ner with whip at his side. He

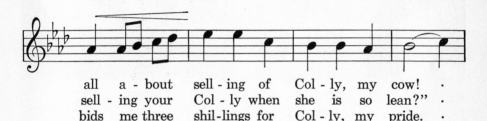

all a - bout sell - ing of Col - ly, my cow! ·
sell - ing your Col - ly when she is so lean?" ·
bids me three shil - lings for Col - ly, my pride. ·

REFRAIN

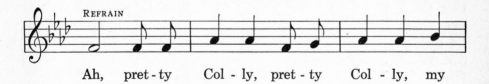

Ah, pret - ty Col - ly, pret - ty Col - ly, my

con espressione   *rall.*

cow! Poor Col - ly will give no more milk to me now!

4. The skin of my Colly
   is softer than silk,
And three times a day
   does my Colly give milk.
Ah, pretty Colly, etc.

5. Then good-by, dear Colly,
   she's gone past recall.
She's sold to a tanner,
   her horns, head, and all.
Ah, pretty Colly, etc.

The Serenade

English version by
Cecil Cowdrey

Spanish-American Folk Song

Dolce cantabile
mp

1. Where jas-mine and rose are swing-ing, · A young trou - ba -
2. Yet far to a dark-eyed maid - en, · The night winds with

dour is sing - ing. · Where jas-mine and rose are
per - fume lad - en, · A - far to that dark - eyed

swing-ing, · He sings in the night a - lone.
maid-en · Are bear-ing each plead-ing tone.

Scratch a Match

Translated by
Carol Fuller

Alsatian Folk Song

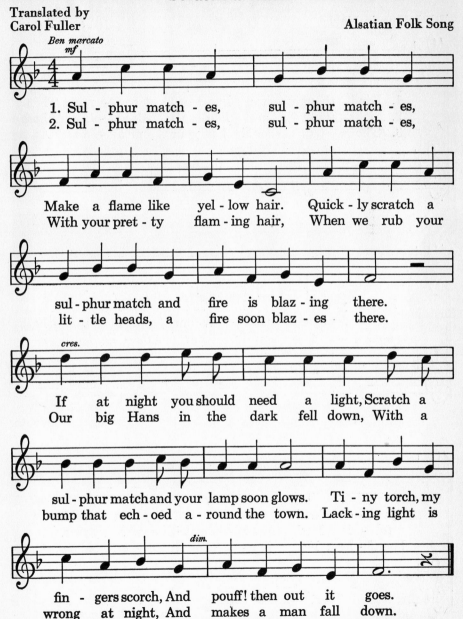

1. Sul - phur match - es, sul - phur match - es,
2. Sul - phur match - es, sul - phur match - es,

Make a flame like yel - low hair. Quick - ly scratch a
With your pret - ty flam - ing hair, When we rub your

sul - phur match and fire is blaz - ing there.
lit - tle heads, a fire soon blaz - es there.

If at night you should need a light, Scratch a
Our big Hans in the dark fell down, With a

sul - phur match and your lamp soon glows. Ti - ny torch, my
bump that ech - oed a - round the town. Lack - ing light is

fin - gers scorch, And pouff! then out it goes.
wrong at night, And makes a man fall down.

Thoughts

Ethel Crowninshield

Jacob Arcadelt

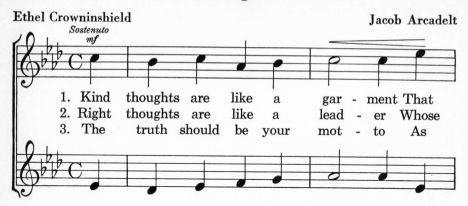

1. Kind thoughts are like a gar - ment That
2. Right thoughts are like a lead - er Whose
3. The truth should be your mot - to As

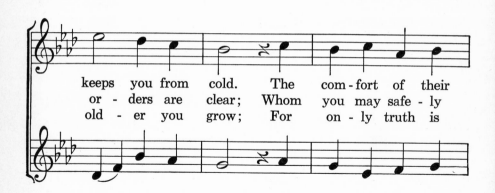

keeps you from cold. The com - fort of their
or - ders are clear; Whom you may safe - ly
old - er you grow; For on - ly truth is

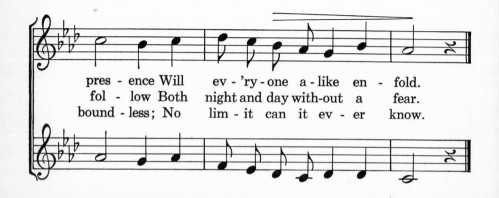

pres - ence Will ev - 'ry-one a - like en - fold.
fol - low Both night and day with-out a fear.
bound - less; No lim - it can it ev - er know.

Translated by
Christine Turner Curtis

Yugoslavian Folk Song

1. Praise the yel - low fruit - ful val - leys,
2. Praise the crim - son ap - ples twin - kling

Praise to the wheat. Praise the fra - grance
High in the leaves. Praise the grape that

of the vine-yards Ris - ing sweet, Ris - ing sweet.
through the trel - lis Pur - ple weaves, Pur - ple weaves.

Frog in the Well

Traditional American   **ROTE**   Traditional American

1. There was a frog lived in a well; Kit-ty a-lone,
2. The frog went to the mous-e's hall; Kit-ty a-lone,
3. Then Mis-tress Mouse came rus-tling down; Kit-ty a-lone,

Kit-ty a-lone. There was a frog lived in a well;
Kit-ty a-lone. The frog went to the mous-e's hall;
Kit-ty a-lone. Then Mis-tress Mouse came rus-tling down;

Kit-ty a-lone and I. · There was a frog lived
Kit-ty a-lone and I. · The frog went to the
Kit-ty a-lone and I. · Then Mis-tress Mouse came

in a well, While a mouse lived in a cell. O
mous-e's hall, Stopped to pay a friend-ly call. O
rus-tling down, Dressed in silk and sat-in gown. O

ALL STANZAS

Frog, my dear-ie, Kit-ty a-lone; Kit-ty a-lone and I. ·

4. "O Mistress Mouse, you look so fine!
Kitty alone, Kitty alone.
O Mistress Mouse, you look so fine!
Kitty alone and I.
O Mistress Mouse, you look so fine!
Tell me, now, will you be mine?"
O Frog, my dearie, etc.

5. "Oh, what a charming thing to say!
Kitty alone, Kitty alone.
Oh, what a charming thing to say!
Kitty alone and I.
Oh, what a charming thing to say!
I'll be yours this very day."
O Frog, my dearie, etc.

Translated by
Amy Clare Giffin

Norwegian Folk Song

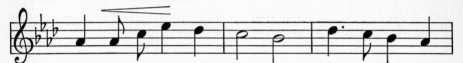

1. The troll of the hill has gold at his will, And
2. "Oh, ring, an-vil, ring, and swing, ham-mer, swing! And
3. But all through the day he hides far a - way, For

steel of the best and whit - est; While the town's a -
ho! for the sword I'm mak - ing!" Hear the mer - ry
this is the troll-man's trou - ble; If he sees one

sleep and still, His forge is burn - ing bright - est.
work - er sing Be - fore the day is break - ing.
sun - ny ray, He'll burst like an - y bub - ble.

In Venice

Marjorie Knapp

Italian Folk Tune

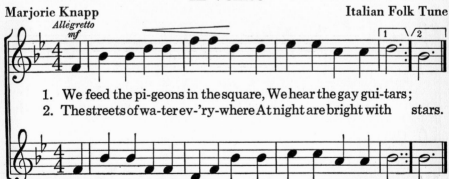

1. We feed the pi-geons in the square, We hear the gay gui-tars;
2. The streets of wa-ter ev-'ry-where At night are bright with stars.

Oldtime Thanksgiving

Hannah Bailey

Clara Edwards

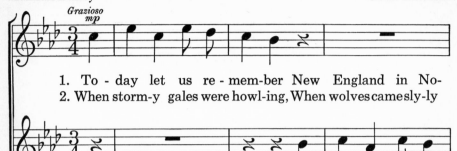

1. To - day let us re - mem-ber New England in No-
2. When storm-y gales were howl-ing, When wolves came sly-ly

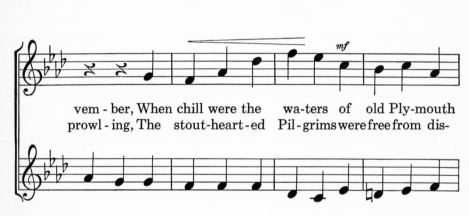

vem - ber, When chill were the wa-ters of old Ply-mouth
prowl-ing, The stout-heart-ed Pil-grims were free from dis-

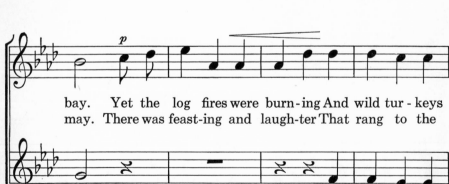

bay. Yet the log fires were burn-ing And wild tur - keys
may. There was feast-ing and laugh-ter That rang to the

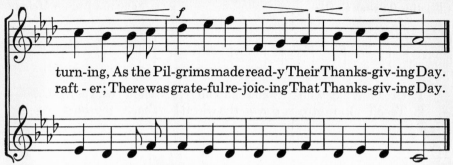

turn-ing, As the Pil-grims made read-y Their Thanks-giv-ing Day.
raft - er; There was grate-ful re-joic-ing That Thanks-giv-ing Day.

Down Green Hills

Translated by
Frances Ford

Inca Folk Song

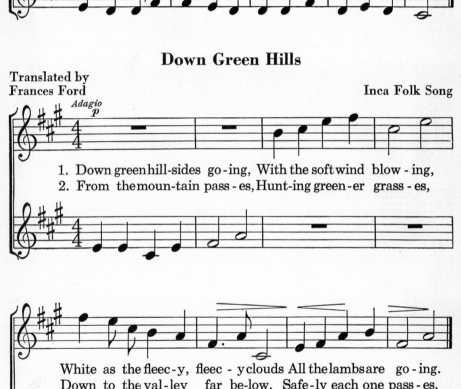

1. Down green hill-sides go-ing, With the soft wind blow-ing,
2. From the moun-tain pass-es, Hunt-ing green-er grass-es,

White as the fleec-y, fleec - y clouds All the lambs are go-ing.
Down to the val-ley   far be-low, Safe-ly each one pass-es.

The Primitive Sculptor

Christine Turner Curtis

Omaha Indian Melody

1. Great Wind who dwells a - bove, Thou who blow - est
2. Teach me to draw the wheat! Teach me how to

from a - far; Oh, lean from the col - ored cloud To
paint the skies, To fash - ion the face of man, To

breathe up - on the In - dian jar! Rain - bow,
make it strong and make it wise! Rain - bow,

red and blue, Oh, arch a - bove the
red and blue, Oh, arch a - bove the

des - ert gray, And teach me how to tint the clay!
des - ert sand, And bless the la - bor of my hand!

The Art Extension Press, Inc.

The Primitive Sculptor

Painted by the American artist EANGER IRVING COUSE

"Rainbow, red and blue,
Oh, arch above the desert gray,
And teach me how to tint the clay!"

Windmill

Nellie Poorman　　　　　　　　　　　　　　　Anna von W. Grille

1. Roar-ing, pour-ing out of the west, Sea breeze,
2. Long arms, strong arms, whirl-ing a - way! Rye meal,

shore breeze, which one is best? Name the most stead - y,
bar - ley, grind me to - day. You'll find it eas - y,

name the most read - y. Tell me, wind-mill, nev-er at rest.
now it is breez-y: Turn then, wind-mill, make no de - lay.

Frederick H. Martens

1. No dar - ing man be - fore him A -
2. He dou - bled in his jour - ney The

round the globe had sailed, Yet o'er the force of
capes where ships are lost; He sailed the spic - y

un - known seas The stur - dy "Gold - en
east - ern seas Where gal - lant ships are

Hind"[1] pre - vailed; All gales out - fac - ing, Fur - rows trac - ing,
rolled and tossed; All risks de - fy - ing, Fame un - dy - ing

Back to Plym - outh town Drake came bold - ly rac - ing.
Crowned him as he came Home with col - ors fly - ing.

[1] Name of ship.

Water Voices

ROTE

Frances Ford

Felix Mendelssohn

Dolce cantabile
mp

1. The brook goes sing - ing night and day A
2. The sea goes sing - ing all day long A

twin - kling tune, a tin - kling tune. It
bub - bling tune, a trou - bling tune. Now

chat - ters in mer - ry talk at noon; It
la - zy and blue, the wa - ters croon A

rip - ples be - neath the sum - mer moon. In
mel - o - dy soft as rain in June. In

cres.   *mf*

win - ter its i - cy wa - ters play Like
win - ter they roar a salt - y song Like

bells · when they jin - gle on a sleigh. ·
notes · of an or - gan, deep and strong. ·

At the Fair

English version by
Clara Louise Kessler

Russian Folk Song

1. Broth - er I - van, broth-er I - van, Will you
2. Broth - er I - van, broth-er I - van, Though I'd

take me to the fair? I'll buy a cor - al
like so man-y things, I've paid my sil - ver

neck - lace Or a rib - bon for my hair.
mon - ey For a bird that sweet-ly sings.

Who Will Buy?

Louise Ayres Garnett

Syrian Folk Tune

1. Who will buy my figs and ol - ives, Glis-t'ning with the
2. There's a haze up - on the moun-tain; Like a gauz - y

ear - ly dew? Sea-green wa - ters seem to dye them,
veil it lies. Sum - mer weaves her silk - en pat-terns

Earth of brown and sky of blue. Sea-green wa - ters
On the back-ground of the skies. Sum-mer weaves her

[1] From the "Botsford Collection of Folk Songs," compiled and edited by Florence Hudson Botsford, Volume I, copyrighted 1922 and 1930 by G. Schirmer, Inc. Printed by permission.

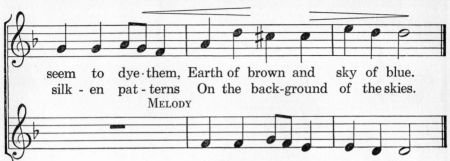

seem to dye·them, Earth of brown and sky of blue.
silk - en pat - terns On the back-ground of the skies.
MELODY

A Chinese Fairy Tale

Marjorie Knapp   Chinese Folk Tune

Moderato
mp

1. Bright blue of the tur-quoise, sea-green of the jade;
2. Foun-tains flow with jew - els, flash with light and shade;

Cor - als, am - ber, o - pals, gems of ev - 'ry shade;
Now there walks a prin - cess clad in rich bro - cade;

cres.

Drag - ons, ma - gi - cians, junks[1] with crim-son sail
Strange the en - chant-ments, strange the sto-ries told

mf

Dec - o- rate the pag - es of this fair - y tale.
Of the Flow-'ry King - dom, col - or - ful and old.

[1] "Junk" is the name of a Chinese boat.

By the Banks of Boyne

Adapted by
Frederick H. Martens

Irish Folk Song

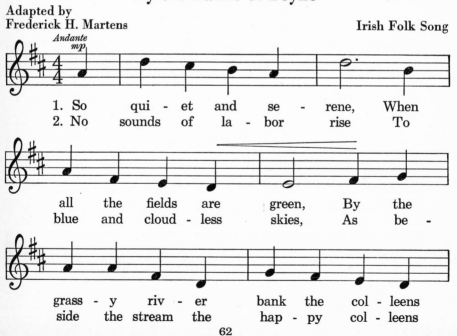

Andante
mp

1. So   qui - et and   se - rene,   When
2. No   sounds of   la - bor   rise   To

all   the   fields   are   green,   By   the
blue   and   cloud - less   skies,   As   be -

grass - y   riv - er   bank   the   col - leens
side   the   stream   the   hap - py   col - leens

stray. · · You can see them pass - ing there, With
play. · · While the wa - ters as they flow Now

shawls a - bout their hair, Each Sun - day as to
seem to mur-mur low, "Oh, sing with joy this

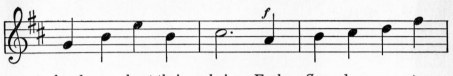

church they wend their way. You see them pass - ing
love - ly sum - mer day!" The wa - ters as they

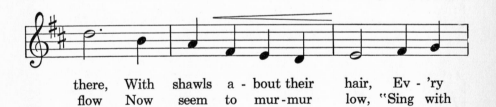

there, With shawls a - bout their hair, Ev - 'ry
flow Now seem to mur -mur low, "Sing with

Sun - day as to church they wend their way.
joy this love - ly, sun - ny sum - mer day."

The Cowboy

From "Singing Cowboy"
Paraphrase

Song of the Plains

Energico
mf

1. My home's in Mon - ta - na, I wear a ban -
2. When val - leys are dust - y, My po - ny is
3. When, far from the ranch - es, I chop the pine

dan - na; My spurs are of sil - ver, My po - ny is
trust - y; He lopes through the bliz-zard, The snow in his
branch - es To heap on my camp-fire As day-light grows

f

gray. When rid - ing the rang - es My luck nev - er
ears. The cat - tle may scat - ter, But what does it
pale; When I have par - tak - en of beans and of

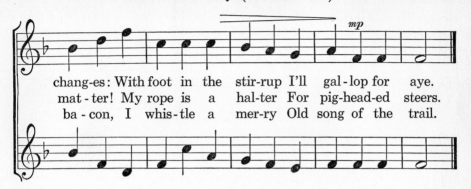

chang-es: With foot in the stir-rup I'll gal-lop for aye.
mat-ter! My rope is a hal-ter For pig-head-ed steers.
ba-con, I whis-tle a mer-ry Old song of the trail.

Call to the Dance

After the original by
Hannah Bailey

Chippewa Indian Melody

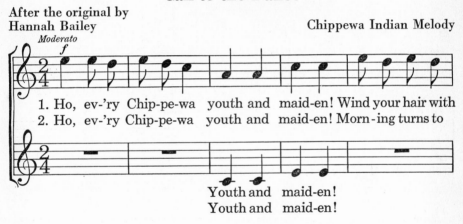

1. Ho, ev-'ry Chip-pe-wa youth and maid-en! Wind your hair with
2. Ho, ev-'ry Chip-pe-wa youth and maid-en! Morn-ing turns to

Youth and maid-en!
Youth and maid-en!

wam-pum, Come to the danc-ing! Hark to the Chip-pe-wa drum!
twi-light; Come to the danc-ing! Loud beats the tom-tom to-night!

Moon Gardens

George Murray Brown

Lily Strickland

1. I know of a moon gar-den fra-grant and
2. My wish-es for friends turn to daf-fo-dils

fair, Where love-li-est flow-ers grow. · The
sweet, And ros-es and as-ters too; · My

wish-es I make turn to blos-soms up there, And
wish-es for clothes turn to hol-ly-hocks neat, Of

wait for me row · on row. · To en-ter my
man-y a rain-bow hue. · My wish-es for

gar-den I dream at night Of wish-es
danc-ing and song are shown By pinks of

made through the day. · I climb up a lad-der of
del-i-cate shade. · A moon gar-den each of us

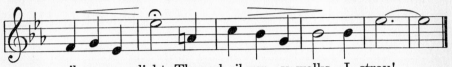

sil-ver - y light; Through sil-ver - y walks I stray!
al-ways may own, By dream-ing of wish - es made.

Sleighing in Russia

Beatrice Wadhams

Russian Folk Tune

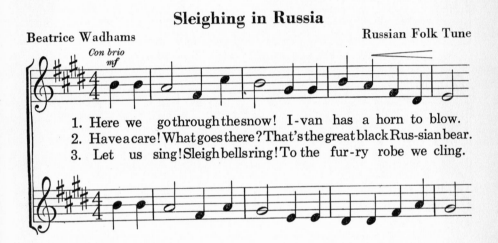

Con brio
mf

1. Here we go through the snow! I-van has a horn to blow.
2. Have a care! What goes there? That's the great black Rus-sian bear.
3. Let us sing! Sleigh bells ring! To the fur-ry robe we cling.

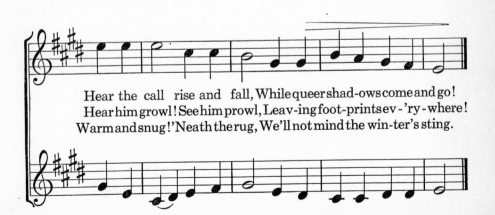

Hear the call rise and fall, While queer shad-ows come and go!
Hear him growl! See him prowl, Leav-ing foot-prints ev - 'ry-where!
Warm and snug! 'Neath the rug, We'll not mind the win-ter's sting.

Song of the Bell

English version by
Nellie Poorman

Friedrich Frischenschlager[1]

1. Ring, O bell of eve-ning time! Bring re-
2. Free the heart from care and woe! Bless the

joic - ing with thy chime! Say that
friend and calm the foe! Bring re -

wea - ry toil may cease. 'Tis the hour of peace.
pose to ev - 'ry - one: Say that day is done!

[1] By permission of the original publishers, Universal Edition, Vienna: contained in "12 Kinderlieder" by Frischenschlager.

English version by
Christine Turner Curtis

French Folk Song

1. Ni - cole, go feed your goose, bird with the
2. Ni - cole, go feed your goat, goat with the

yel - low, yel-low bill, White as the feath - ered thorn
shag - gy, shag-gy head, Gray as the fall - en leaf

high on the hill! Mil - let and bar - ley and
with-ered and dead! Chick - weed and clo - ver to

peas that you scat - ter, scat - ter loose;
bright - en his hair - y, hair - y coat.

Ni - cole, go feed your goose corn from the mill!
Ni - cole, go feed your goat grain from the shed!

The Lighthouse

Irwin M. Cassel

Mana-Zucca

I can see the lamp that's burn - ing In the

light-house on the coast, As it throws its beam to ships pass-ing

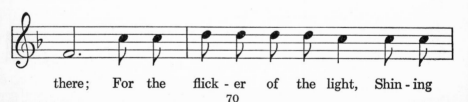

there; For the flick - er of the light, Shin - ing

on through the night, Tells the pass - ing mar - i - ner, "Be -

ware!" The rock - y coast is dan - ger - ous To

ships and sail - or - men, But the

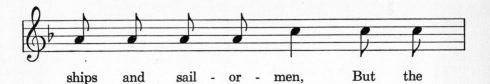

light-house stands as sen - ti - nel brave. And the

light gives its warn-ing Till the com - ing of morn-ing, Sav-ing

ship and sail - or from the cru - el wave.

You Seemed Like a Flower

English version by
George Murray Brown

Inca Melody

1. One sum - mer day you seemed like a flow'r, ·
2. One sum - mer day you seemed like a flow'r, ·

Like one just o - pened at dawn-ing's hour. ·
One of frail beau - ty, yet one of pow'r. ·

Bright eyes smiled?
Pale cheeks flamed?

Was it be - cause your bright eyes were smil - ing,
Was it be - cause your pale cheeks were flam - ing,

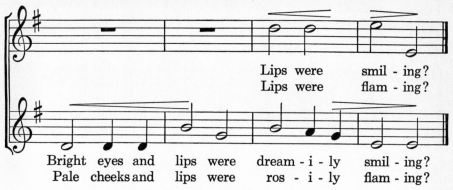

Lips were smil - ing?
Lips were flam - ing?

Bright eyes and lips were dream - i - ly smil - ing?
Pale cheeks and lips were ros - i - ly flam - ing?

Bells

Ethel Crowninshield   Lettish Folk Tune

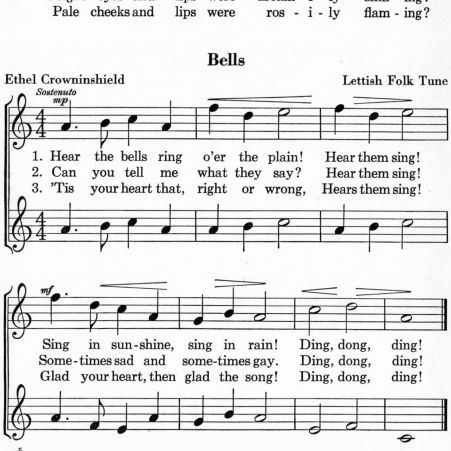

1. Hear the bells ring o'er the plain! Hear them sing!
2. Can you tell me what they say? Hear them sing!
3. 'Tis your heart that, right or wrong, Hears them sing!

Sing in sun-shine, sing in rain! Ding, dong, ding!
Some-times sad and some-times gay. Ding, dong, ding!
Glad your heart, then glad the song! Ding, dong, ding!

5

The Fisher Maiden

Translated by
Carol Fuller

French Folk Song

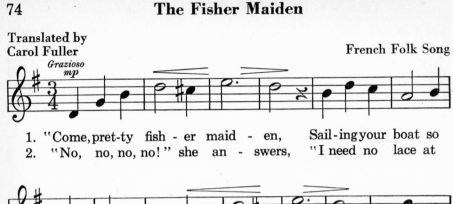

1. "Come, pret-ty fish - er maid - en, Sail-ing your boat so
2. "No, no, no, no!" she an - swers, "I need no lace at

free; · Look where my cas - tle ris - es! Will you not
all. · Look how the foam is weav - ing Pat-terns that

mar - ry me? · Blos-soms I'll bring, fresh as the
rise and fall. · Sea-weeds that float, close by my

spring; Ru - bies, lac - es I'll buy, · Gifts that are
boat, Make a gar-den for me. · I would not

glad sur - pris - es. No prince will be proud as I." ·
dream of leav - ing My home near the shin - ing sea." ·

Rose Fyleman

George Frederick Handel

Larghetto

1. Once there lived a might - y king
2. If you turned it on your hand,
3. Should he ask for fame or wealth,

Who pos - sessed a mag - ic ring
You of for - tune might de - mand
Wis - dom, glo - ry, hon - ors, health?

Wrought of gold, fine and fair,
An - y wish, great or small;
Old he grew! still de - layed,

Set a - bout with jew - els rare. Strange and po - tent
On - ly one, and that was all. But the king could
And the choice was yet un - made, Till he passed be -

was its spell, But the mon - arch loved it well.
not de - cide How the boon should be ap - plied.
yond re - call; Nev - er had his wish at all!

Remembrance

Carol Fuller

Johannes Brahms

1. In win - ter time we all re - mem - ber How pink our
2. In sum - mer time with heat de - scend - ing, And wa - ter -

ros - es used to grow. And e - ven though it's cold De -
lil - ies o - p'ning too, We think of snow - y branch - es

cem - ber, We think of wait - ing buds Deep un - der snow.
bend - ing By lakes of gleam - ing ice, Daz - zling and blue.

King Arthur's Land

Richard Gage

Welsh Folk Tune

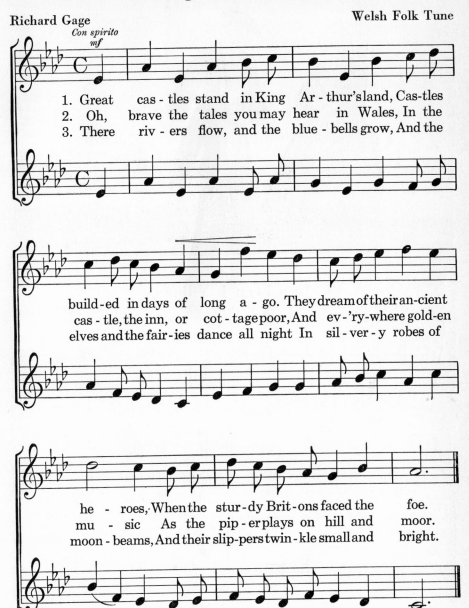

1. Great cas-tles stand in King Ar-thur's land, Cas-tles
2. Oh, brave the tales you may hear in Wales, In the
3. There riv-ers flow, and the blue-bells grow, And the

build-ed in days of long a-go. They dream of their an-cient
cas-tle, the inn, or cot-tage poor, And ev-'ry-where gold-en
elves and the fair-ies dance all night In sil-ver-y robes of

he-roes, When the stur-dy Brit-ons faced the foe.
mu-sic As the pip-er plays on hill and moor.
moon-beams, And their slip-pers twin-kle small and bright.

In a French Village

Rose Fyleman

French Folk Tune

Andantino
mp

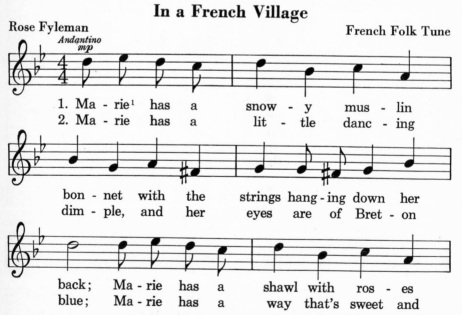

1. Ma - rie[1] has a snow - y mus - lin
2. Ma - rie has a lit - tle danc - ing

bon - net with the strings hang - ing down her
dim - ple, and her eyes are of Bret - on

back; Ma - rie has a shawl with ros - es
blue; Ma - rie has a way that's sweet and

[1] The accent here is on the first syllable.

78

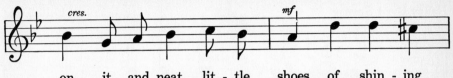

on it and neat lit - tle shoes of shin - ing
sim - ple, and well do I know her heart is

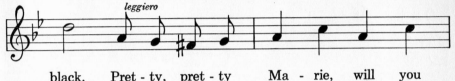

black. Pret - ty, pret - ty Ma - rie, will you
true. Pret - ty, pret - ty Ma - rie, will you

wed? Pret - ty Ma - rie, pray do not shake your
wed? Pret - ty Ma - rie, pray do not shake your

head. I have got a hun - dred fine ap - ple
head. I have got a horse, a pig and a

trees; On - ly do, on - ly do say yes to me, please!
cow; Will you not, will you not say yes to me now?

Arranging Flowers

Nancy Byrd Turner

Japanese Folk Tune

1. Take a vase of slen-der form, Crys-tal, gold, or blue;
2. Find a pool as clear as glass, Clear as glass and still.

Place it where the light is warm, Where a breeze blows through.
Scat-ter pet-als as you pass; Choose them as you will.

Fill it with mag-no-lia bloom Fresh with dew and fair.
Blue or yel-low, pink or white, Shal-low boats they'll be,

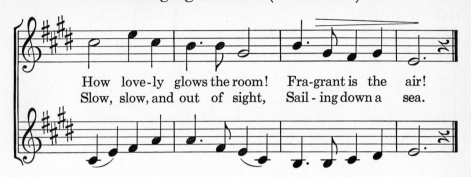

How love-ly glows the room! Fra-grant is the air!
Slow, slow, and out of sight, Sail - ing down a sea.

The Yellow Rose

English version by
Christine Turner Curtis

Spanish Folk Song

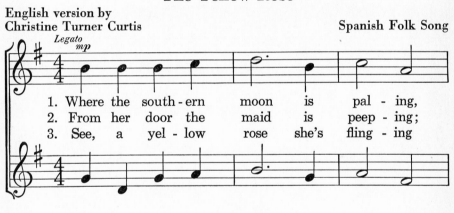

Legato
mp

1. Where the south - ern moon is pal - ing,
2. From her door the maid is peep - ing;
3. See, a yel - low rose she's fling - ing

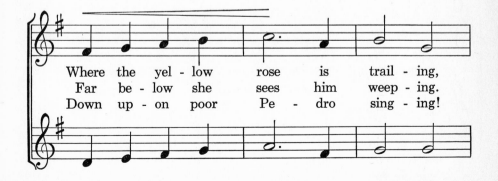

Where the yel - low rose is trail - ing,
Far be - low she sees him weep - ing.
Down up - on poor Pe - dro sing - ing!

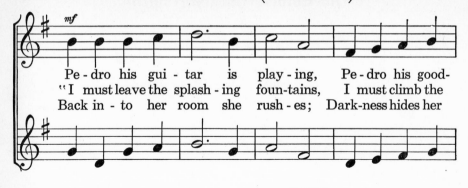

Pe - dro his gui - tar is play - ing, Pe - dro his good-
"I must leave the splash - ing foun - tains, I must climb the
Back in - to her room she rush - es; Dark - ness hides her

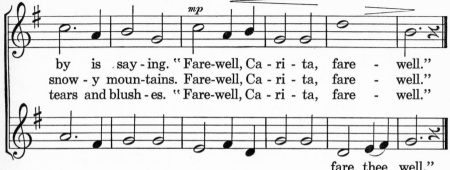

by is say - ing. "Fare-well, Ca - ri - ta, fare - well."
snow - y moun-tains. Fare-well, Ca - ri - ta, fare - well."
tears and blush - es. "Fare-well, Ca - ri - ta, fare - well."

fare thee well."
fare thee well."
fare thee well."

An Old Chinese Garden

Susanna Myers ROTE Bainbridge Crist

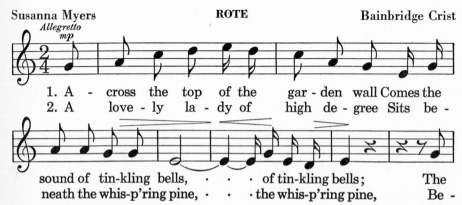

1. A - cross the top of the gar - den wall Comes the
2. A love - ly la - dy of high de - gree Sits be -

sound of tin-kling bells, · · · of tin-kling bells; The
neath the whis-p'ring pine, · · · the whis-p'ring pine, Be -

wind blows soft through the whis - p'ring pines, And the
side the pool where the gold - fish dart, And the

mu - sic grows and swells, · · of tin-kling bells. The
yel-low sun-beams shine, · · the sun-beams shine. She

foun - tain drips in the qui - et pool, Set a -
sings a song of the old - en days, And her

bout with glis-t'ning shells, · · with glis-t'ning shells.
voice is like the bells, · · the sil-v'ry bells.

The air is ring - ing with sil - v'ry sounds And the
Her song floats o - ver the gar - den wall With the

chime of tin - kling bells, · · of tin-kling bells.
chime of tin - kling bells, · · of tin-kling bells.

Christmas Carol

After the original by
Susanna Myers

ROTE

Old Danish Carol

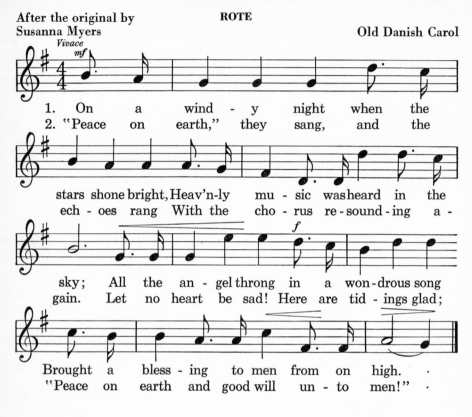

Vivace
mf

1. On a wind - y night when the
stars shone bright, Heav'n-ly mu - sic was heard in the
sky; All the an - gel throng in a won-drous song
Brought a bless - ing to men from on high.

2. "Peace on earth," they sang, and the
ech - oes rang With the cho - rus re - sound - ing a -
gain. Let no heart be sad! Here are tid - ings glad;
"Peace on earth and good will un - to men!"

Long, Long Ago

Author unknown

Sally Bowen

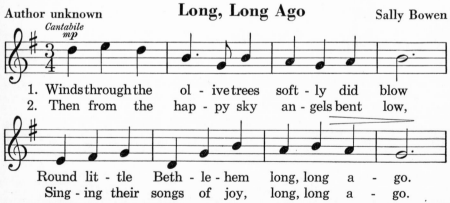

Cantabile
mp

1. Winds through the ol - ive trees soft - ly did blow
Round lit - tle Beth - le - hem long, long a - go.

2. Then from the hap - py sky an - gels bent low,
Sing - ing their songs of joy, long, long a - go.

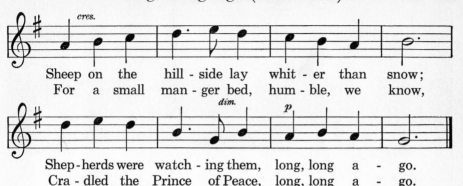

Sheep on the hill - side lay whit - er than snow;
For a small man - ger bed, hum - ble, we know,

Shep - herds were watch - ing them, long, long a - go.
Cra - dled the Prince of Peace, long, long a - go.

Rejoice, Ye Bells

English version by
Christine Turner Curtis

French Noel

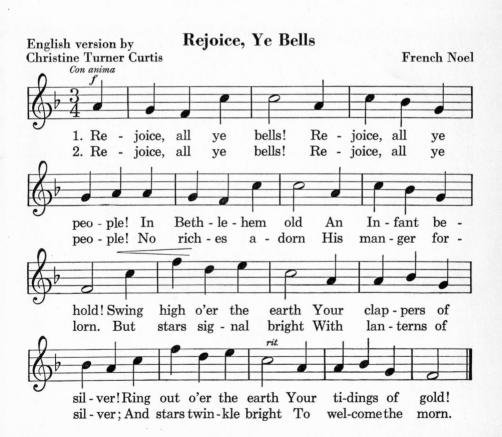

1. Re - joice, all ye bells! Re - joice, all ye
2. Re - joice, all ye bells! Re - joice, all ye

peo - ple! In Beth - le - hem old An In - fant be -
peo - ple! No rich - es a - dorn His man - ger for -

hold! Swing high o'er the earth Your clap - pers of
lorn. But stars sig - nal bright With lan - terns of

sil - ver! Ring out o'er the earth Your ti - dings of gold!
sil - ver; And stars twin - kle bright To wel - come the morn.

Carol

After the original by
Marjorie Knapp

Bavarian Carol

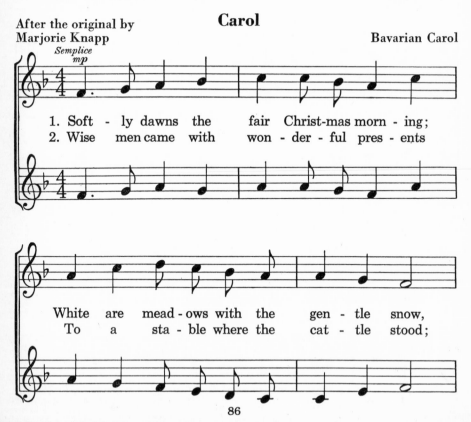

1. Soft - ly dawns the fair Christ-mas morn - ing;
2. Wise men came with won - der - ful pres - ents

White are mead - ows with the gen - tle snow,
To a sta - ble where the cat - tle stood;

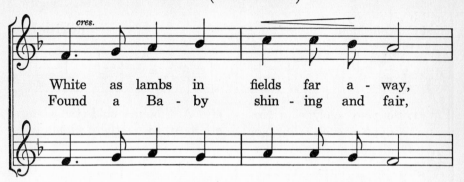

White   as lambs   in   fields   far   a - way,
Found   a   Ba - by   shin - ing   and   fair,

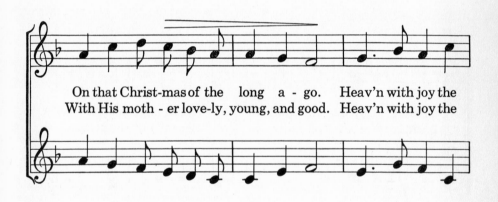

On that Christ-mas of the   long a - go.   Heav'n with joy the
With His moth - er love-ly, young, and good.   Heav'n with joy the

sto - ry tells.   Earth re-joice and sing! Ring   out,   O bells!
sto - ry tells.   Earth re-joice and sing! Ring   out,   O bells!

Sing Noel

English version by
Ethel Crowninshield

Belgian Noel

Con moto

1. Sing No - el, sing No - el! Al-though cold the winds
2. Sing No - el, sing No - el! Sing to those who are

blow; Sing No - el, sing No - el! Al-though deep is the
sad! Sing No - el, sing No - el! Sing to those who are

snow. 'Tis the night be - fore Christ-mas, so fill it with
glad! Sing to ev - 'ry - one, ev - 'ry-where, both great and

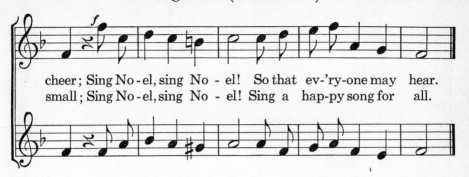

cheer; Sing No-el, sing No - el! So that ev-'ry-one may hear.
small; Sing No-el, sing No - el! Sing a hap-py song for all.

The Roads Are Very Dusty[1]

ROTE

English Traditional   Traditional Hampshire

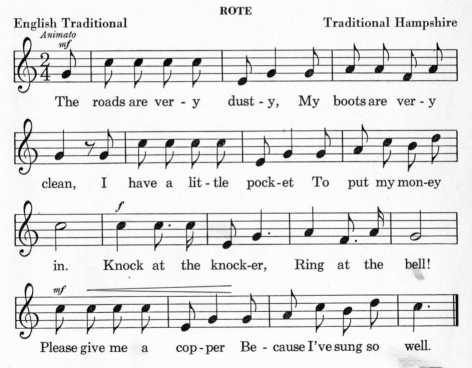

The roads are ver - y dust-y, My boots are ver - y

clean, I have a lit-tle pock-et To put my mon-ey

in. Knock at the knock-er, Ring at the bell!

Please give me a cop-per Be-cause I've sung so well.

[1] From Motherland Songs, Eight Traditional Carols. Used by permission of Stainer and Bell, Ltd., owners of the copyright.

Christmas Angels

After the original by
Carol Fuller

Czech Christmas Carol

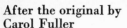

1. An - gels, an - gels, sing-ing in the skies, Show us the
2. An - gels, an - gels, lead us through the years! Glad - ly we

place where our Christ-mas Ba-by lies.   Is He   cold with
fol - low, for - get-ting all our fears.   Think of   Him Whose

straw for His   bed?   Is   it   dark out   there in a
light was a   star,   Then no Heav'n will   seem ver - y

shed?   No, for   light sur - rounds His sleep-ing   form;
far.   Know that   He will   keep us safe from   harm.

Through win - ter   dark - ness His love can keep us   warm.
Through cold and   dark - ness His ten-der heart is   warm.

ROTE

Mary Smith

Belgian Noel

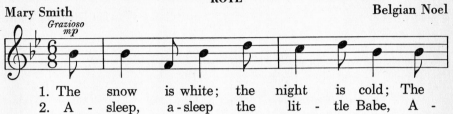

1. The snow is white; the night is cold; The
2. A - sleep, a - sleep the lit - tle Babe, A -

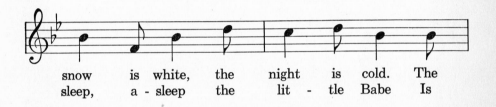

snow is white, the night is cold. The
sleep, a - sleep the lit - tle Babe Is

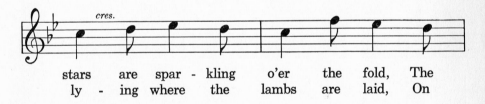

stars are spar - kling o'er the fold, The
ly - ing where the lambs are laid, On

lit - tle Child is sleep - ing. Will sheep and cat - tle
hay that grew in sum - mer; On hay that grew to

keep Him warm, The lit - tle Child who's sleep - ing?
keep Him warm, The lit - tle, sweet New - com - er.

The Light Heart

After the original by
Eleanor Farjeon

Italian Folk Song

1. I'd rath - er far be low - ly, With -
2. I'd rath - er wed my Li - sa, My

out a care or sor - row, Than be the sul - tan
pret - ty loy - al maid - en, Than own the tow'r of

ho - ly And gov - ern Tur - ke - stan! My
Pi - sa, Or dwell in Pe - ter's dome! My

ox - en are the whit - est That plow the Tus - can
lem - on trees are bright - est, My fig trees heav - y

fur - row; My heart, my heart's the
lad - en; My heart, my heart's the

light - est From Na - ples to Mi - lan!
light - est From Gen - o - a to Rome!

Children of Kildare

After the original by
Ethel Crowninshield

Irish Folk Song

1. Twi - light hov - ers o - ver - all;
2. From the sea the wind will - rise;

Sleep, my child, the shad - ows fall. While you dream, the
Sleep, my child, and close your eyes. God keep those who

stars on high Walk in si - lence through the sky;
have to roam, God keep those who bide at home.

Hold - ing up their lamps with care O'er the chil - dren
God keep those who far must fare From the Coun - ty

of Kil - dare. Peace is rest - ing still and - deep
of Kil - dare. God keep all with - in His - sight,

O'er Kil - dare when chil - dren sleep, chil - dren sleep.
'Til they hear the last good-night, last good - night.

Coasting Song

Rose Fyleman

Austrian Folk Tune

Con spirito

1. O - ver the sil - ver snow Gay - ly our sledg - es go.
2. Down-ward the run-ners speed, Still tak - ing care - ful heed,

Bright are the moun-tains, Bright and frost-y is the air.
Watch-ful and wa - ry, Stead - y eye and read-y hand.

Swift - er than ea-gles glide; Thus might a he - ro ride On
Mon-archs could nev-er be Half so con - tent as we. We're

chiv - al - rous quest, To ad - ven-ture and to dare.
lords of de - light In a fair en-chant-ed land.

If You Could Change

Nancy Byrd Turner

German Folk Tune

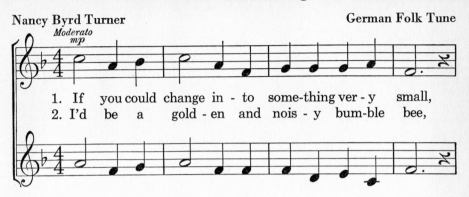

1. If you could change in-to some-thing ver-y small,
2. I'd be a gold-en and nois-y bum-ble bee,

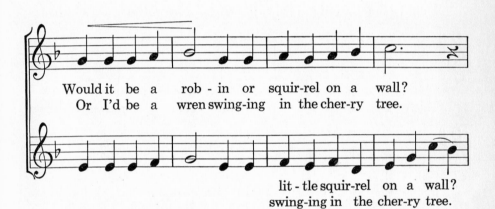

Would it be a rob-in or squir-rel on a wall?
Or I'd be a wren swing-ing in the cher-ry tree.

lit-tle squir-rel on a wall?
swing-ing in the cher-ry tree.

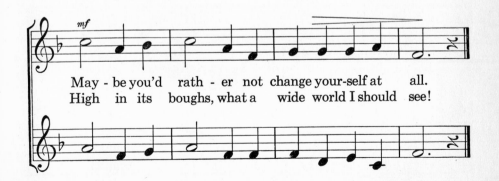

May-be you'd rath-er not change your-self at all.
High in its boughs, what a wide world I should see!

Drifting Snow

Nancy Byrd Turner
Adapted

Anna von W. Grille

Andante
mp

1. Cold the stars are shin - ing on the
2. Lone - ly is our house where dark and

drift - ed white snow; Through the gloom - y
chill the hearth grows; In the gray - ing

for - est cold the win - ter winds blow.
ash - es on - ly one red coal glows.

mf   *mf*

Sleigh-bells bright, ring - ing sil - ver, sweet and light,
Blow with might till the room is all a - light;

Sound - ing clear where fields lie white.
Then bring can - dles tall and white.

Sleigh-bells in the star - ry cold night!
Let the star - ry can - dles burn bright!

Moral Song

John Farrar

Mary Root Kern

Giocoso
mf

1. Oh, so cool in his deep green
2. Now that frog left his own home
3. With a swish came a might - y

pool Was a frog on a log one day, Was a
log; And he start - ed a - way to play, And he
fish And he swal-lowed him where he lay, And he

frog on a log one day! He would blink his eyes and
start-ed a-way to play. Oh, he flopped and flopped and
swal-lowed him where he lay. Now it's things like this that

snap at flies; For his moth - er was a - way, His
nev - er stopped Till he reached the great blue bay, The
nev - er miss Lit-tle frogs who don't o - bey, The

f   *rall. e dim.*

moth - er, his moth - er, Yes, his moth - er was a - way.
blue bay, the blue bay, Till he reached the great blue bay.
small frogs, the small frogs, Yes, the frogs who don't o - bey.

Lullaby of an Infant Chief

Sir Walter Scott

Clayton Johns

Larghetto

1. Oh, hush thee, my ba-by, thy sire was a knight, Thy
2. Oh, fear not the bu-gle, though loud-ly it blows! It
3. Oh, hush thee, my ba-by, the time soon will come When thy

moth-er a la-dy both love-ly and bright. The
calls but the ward-ers that guard thy re-pose. Their
sleep shall be bro-ken by trum-pet and drum. Then

woods and the glens, from the tow'rs which we see, They
bows would be bend-ed, their blades would be red, Ere the
hush thee, my dar-ling, take rest while you may, For

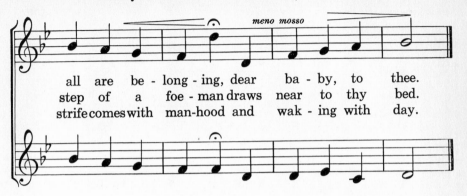

all   are   be - long - ing, dear   ba - by,   to   thee.
step   of   a   foe - man draws   near   to thy   bed.
strife comes with   man-hood and   wak - ing with   day.

West Wind

Susanna Myers

Czech Folk Tune

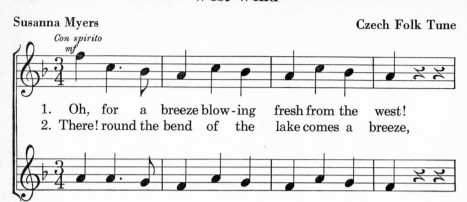

1. Oh, for a breeze blow-ing fresh from the west!
2. There! round the bend of the lake comes a breeze,

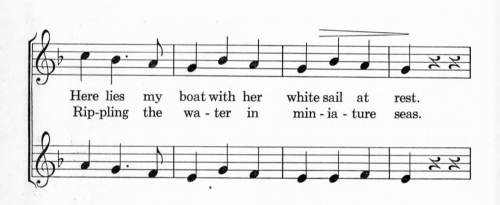

Here lies my boat with her white sail at rest.
Rip-pling the wa-ter in min-ia-ture seas.

Bright is the day; still we must stay,
Quick-ly a-way! No more de-lay;

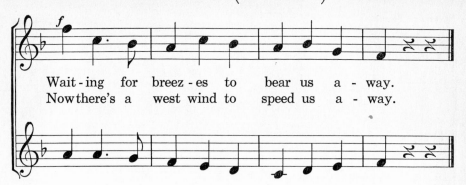

Wait - ing for breez - es to bear us a - way.
Now there's a west wind to speed us a - way.

The Exile

George Murray Brown

Helen S. Leavitt

Sostenuto

1. Win - ter sun a - dorns with jew - els
2. Boys and girls are blithe - ly ski - ing

poco più moto

Snow - y trees of Fin - land; Yet my eyes may
Long - ing eyes may

Down the hills of Fin - land; Yet I may not
Nev - er may I

a tempo

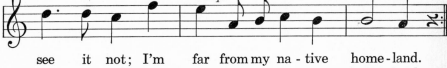

see it not; I'm far from my na - tive home - land.
see it not; I'm far from my na - tive home - land.
join them there; I'm far from my na - tive home - land.
join them there; I'm far from my na - tive home - land,

The Crooked Man

Mother Goose

E. S. Hosmer

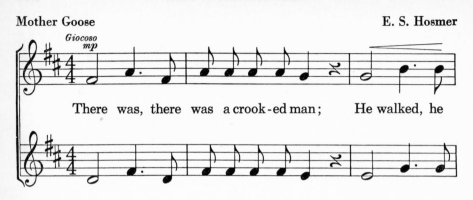

There was, there was a crook-ed man; He walked, he

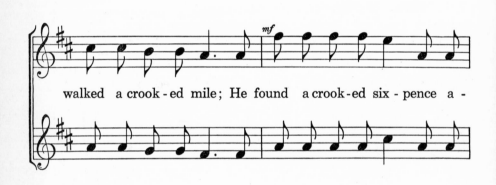

walked a crook-ed mile; He found a crook-ed six-pence a-

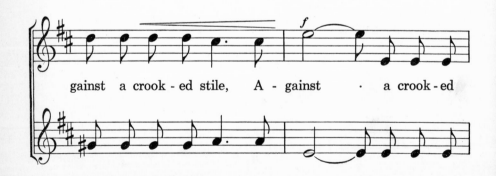

gainst a crook-ed stile, A-gainst · a crook-ed

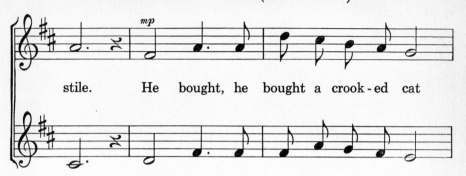

stile.　　He　bought, he　bought a　crook-ed　cat

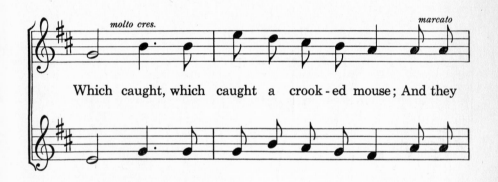

Which　caught, which　caught　a　crook-ed　mouse; And they

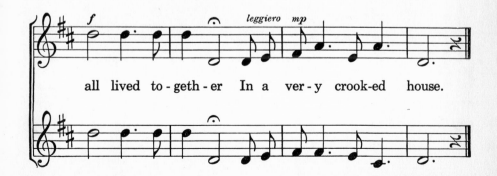

all　lived to-geth-er　In a　ver-y　crook-ed　house.

Charlie

Traditional American
Adapted

Traditional American

1. Char-lie's neat from head to feet, Char-lie's quick and
2. Who could eat your com-mon wheat? Who could eat your

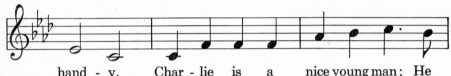

hand - y. Char - lie is a nice young man; He
bar - ley? All I wish is gold - en corn To

poco più moto

feeds his friends on can - dy. Rise you up in the morn-ing
bake a cake for Char-lie. Rise you up in the morn-ing

cres. *f*

Ear - ly all to - geth-er! You need not feel at
Ear - ly all to - geth-er! You need not feel at

all a - fraid Of rain or cloud - y weath - er.
all a - fraid Of rain or cloud - y weath - er.

Mabel Livingstone

Mana-Zucca

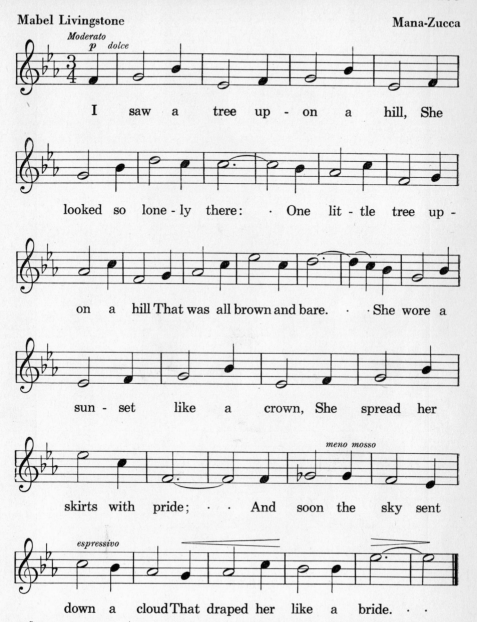

I saw a tree up - on a hill, She

looked so lone - ly there: · One lit - tle tree up -

on a hill That was all brown and bare. · ·She wore a

sun - set like a crown, She spread her

skirts with pride; · · And soon the sky sent

down a cloud That draped her like a bride. · ·

5

Abraham Lincoln

By the American sculptor AUGUSTUS ST. GAUDENS.
The statue is now in Lincoln Park, Chicago

Christine Turner Curtis   **Mary B. Black**

Moderato
mf

1. There's a brown log cab - in stand - ing in the
2. On the hearth the pine - knot flick - ered with a
3. Now the ring - ing ax is si - lent un - der

blue Ken - tuck - y hills; And the for - est sweeps a -
qui - et yel - low cheer; In the flames a boy was
blue Ken - tuck - y skies; But the name of Lin - coln

round it with the song of whip - poor -
gaz - ing, and his eyes were blue and
stirs us, for his glo - ry nev - er

wills; There the In - dian corn was grow - ing, and a
clear. Did he see dark vi - sions ris - ing of his
dies. And his love of coun - try fires us to a

boy, in buck-skin clad, Swung his ax be - neath the
coun - try torn and sad? Did he vow his heart would
serv - ice proud and glad, As we think up - on that

south - ern pine, When Lin - coln was a lad.
loy - al be, When Lin - coln was a lad?
by - gone day When Lin - coln was a lad.

Pepita

Translated by
Frances Ford

Spanish Folk Song

Grazioso
mf

1. Sau - cy and dark is Pe - pi - ta,
2. Now see her spin - ning and whirl - ing,

Nev - er a rose could be sweet - er.
All her red rib - bons un - furl - ing!

When she comes click - ing her cas - ta - nets,
See how she flut - ters her cor - al fan,

Not a foot could be neat - er.
Gay - ly trip - ping and twirl - ing!

Marjorie Knapp

Motion

Italian Folk Tune

Leggiero
mf

1. Boats go sail - ing far o - ver the sea;
2. Birds go wing - ing; how swift-ly they fly!

p

Clouds go trail - ing, white, fluff - y, and free.
We'll go swing - ing 'way up to the sky.

Jolly Winter

Richard Gage

Swedish Folk Tune

Vivace
mf

1. Wind through the pine trees is blow - ing;
2. Come now, no time for de - lay - ing!

Fac - es are rud - dy and glow - ing.
Come, jol - ly win - ter o - bey - ing!

f

Bring out the snow-shoes, the skates, the skis!
Er - ic and Pe - ter and Ol - ga too;

Win - ter is here with its snow - ing.
We must be off for the sleigh - ing.

Queen Venice

Hannah Bailey

Gaetano Donizetti

Con moto
mf

1. Trum - pets blow - ing, gild - ed barg - es row - ing;
2. Ros - es rain - ing, all the rip - ples stain - ing;
3. Church bells ring - ing, prince and peo - ple sing - ing;

Ven - ice, rule for - ev - er, cit - y of the sea!
Crown her queen for - ev - er, cit - y of the sea!
Ven - ice, loved for - ev - er, cit - y of the sea!

The Magic Harp

Translated by
Luther Wilde

Finnish Folk Song

Dolce espressivo

1. Ul - fra plays her gold - en harp;
2. Through the for - est steals the tune;

Ting - a - ling, ting - a - loo. Fierce black wolves with
Ting - a - ling, ting - a - loo. Night - in - gales for -

eyes that glis - ten Fold their fur - ry paws to lis - ten.
get their sing - ing; Now the charm sets blue - bells spring - ing.

Ting - a - ling, ting - a - loo. Gold - en harp!
Ting - a - ling, ting - a - loo. Gold - en harp!

Susanna Myers

Holiday

Austrian Folk Tune

Animato

1. No books or les - sons to - day; · We're
2. Yes, that's the name for a day · So

free for all kinds of play. · The weath-er is per-fect for
free for all kinds of play. · See, here on the cal - en - dar

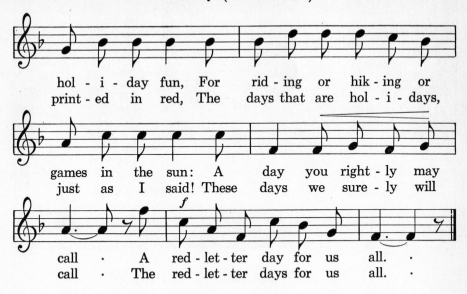

hol - i - day fun, For rid - ing or hik - ing or
print - ed in red, The days that are hol - i - days,

games in the sun: A day you right - ly may
just as I said! These days we sure - ly will

call · A red - let - ter day for us all. ·
call · The red - let - ter days for us all. ·

Winter Birds

Mary Smith

Norwegian Folk Tune

1. Cold is the win - ter in Nor - way;
2. Chil - dren in snow - cov - ered Nor - way

Birds are black a - gainst the snow. Hun - gry, they cir - cle the
Scat - ter food where birds can see, Hang - ing it high on the

farm - house, Search - ing high and low. ·
house - tops, High on roof and tree. ·

Pencil and Paint

ROTE

Eleanor Farjeon
Second stanza by Hannah Bailey

Carl Busch

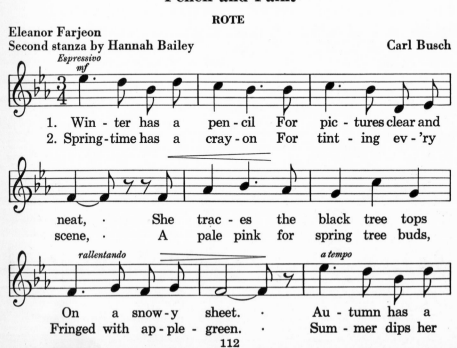

Espressivo
mf

1. Win - ter has a pen - cil For pic - tures clear and
2. Spring - time has a cray - on For tint - ing ev - 'ry

neat, · She trac - es the black tree tops
scene, · A pale pink for spring tree buds,

rallentando — *a tempo*

On a snow - y sheet. · Au - tumn has a
Fringed with ap - ple - green. · Sum - mer dips her

112

pal - ette And a paint - ing brush in - stead, · And
brush - es In the sun so bright and old, · She

daubs the leaves for pleas-ure With yel-low, brown, and red.
trims each leaf and blos-som With pure and shin-ing gold.

Sea Horses

Clara Louise Kessler   Jamaican Folk Tune

1. Gal - lop - ing in with the eve - ning tide,
2. Now they are clos - er and wild with fear,

Wild and free, hors - es stride; Gal - lop - ing, gal - lop - ing,
Snow - y manes toss - ing near. Hors - es, what fright-ens and

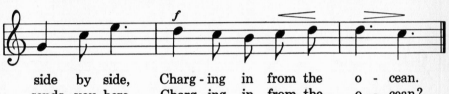

side by side, Charg - ing in from the o - cean.
sends you here, Charg - ing in from the o - cean?

The Giant

Louise Ayres Garnett

Yugoslavian Folk Tune

1. Once a gi - ant came a - wan - der - ing
2. When he reached the high - est part of it,
3. "Gi - ant, Gi - ant, I am un - der you,

Late at night when the world was still; Seek - ing for a
Sat him down on its ver - y peak; Lit - tle Hill cried
Move, or this is the last of me!" But the Gi - ant

stool to sit on, He climbed a lit - tle green hill! ·
out at once in A faint and far - a - way squeak.
an-swered, "Thank you! I like it here, don't you see?"

The Peddler

English version by
Christine Turner Curtis

French-Canadian Folk Song

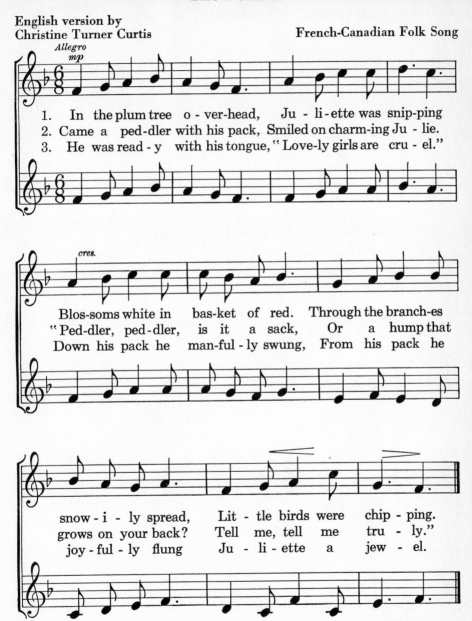

1. In the plum tree o-ver-head, Ju-li-ette was snip-ping
2. Came a ped-dler with his pack, Smiled on charm-ing Ju-lie.
3. He was read-y with his tongue, "Love-ly girls are cru-el."

Blos-soms white in bas-ket of red. Through the branch-es
"Ped-dler, ped-dler, is it a sack, Or a hump that
Down his pack he man-ful-ly swung, From his pack he

snow-i-ly spread, Lit-tle birds were chip-ping.
grows on your back? Tell me, tell me tru-ly."
joy-ful-ly flung Ju-li-ette a jew-el.

Tomorrow

(MAÑANA)

After the original by
Frances Ford

Spanish-American Folk Song

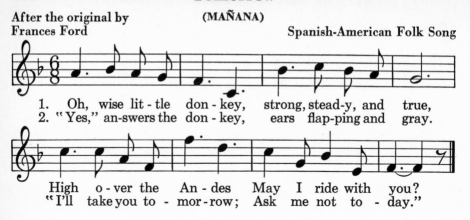

1. Oh, wise lit - tle don - key, strong, stead-y, and true,
2. "Yes," an-swers the don - key, ears flap-ping and gray.

High o - ver the An - des May I ride with you?
"I'll take you to - mor-row; Ask me not to - day."

Mr. Fox and Mrs. Hare

Rose Fyleman
Con spirito
mf

ROTE

French Folk Tune

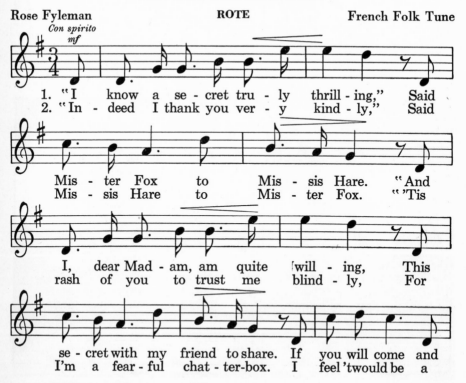

1. "I know a se - cret tru - ly thrill - ing," Said
2. "In - deed I thank you ver - y kind - ly," Said

Mis - ter Fox to Mis - sis Hare. "And
Mis - sis Hare to Mis - ter Fox. " 'Tis

I, dear Mad - am, am quite will - ing, This
rash of you to trust me blind - ly, For

se - cret with my friend to share. If you will come and
I'm a fear - ful chat - ter-box. I feel 'twould be a

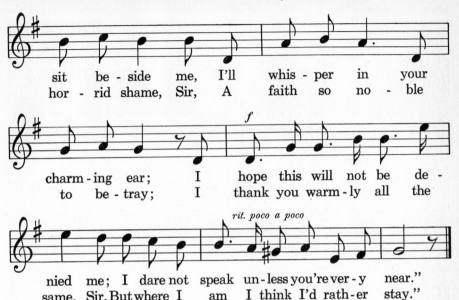

sit be-side me, I'll whis-per in your
hor-rid shame, Sir, A faith so no-ble

f

charm-ing ear; I hope this will not be de-
to be-tray; I thank you warm-ly all the

rit. poco a poco

nied me; I dare not speak un-less you're ver-y near."
same, Sir, But where I am I think I'd rath-er stay."

The Driver

English version by
Cecil Cowdrey

Russian Folk Song

Con spirito

1. With the hors-es in flight, · ·Like a bird the moon
2. Shake your manes curled with frost, · ·Toss them high as you

flies; · ·White with sil-ver a-gleam, · ·White and
go. · ·Past the for-est we speed, · ·Furs all

still the land lies. · ·Gay-ly ring, lit-tle
cov-ered with snow. · ·Gay-ly ring, lit-tle

bells, · ·Sing-ing clear, sing-ing bright! · ·On, my
bells, · ·Ring and light-en the load! · There's a

brave hors-es three! ·Gal-lop on through the night! ·
gate will swing wide ·At the end of the road. ·

Rain

Marjorie Knapp

Dutch Folk Tune

Andantino

1. Now the rain · falls a - gain. Down the win-dow it's
2. By and by, · all the sky Col - ors rare will be

stream - ing; Gray and sil - ver it's gleam - ing.
show - ing Where the rain-bow is glow - ing;

Now the rain, the cool rain falls a - gain. ·
By and by a rain - bow in the sky. ·

Summer Is A-Coming In

**Traditional
Adapted by
Frances Ford**

English Folk Song

1. Sum-mer is a-com-ing in; · Loud-ly sing, cuck-
2. On the hills the lambs do run; · Loud-ly sing, cuck-

oo! · Blows the rose, and blos-soms the lil-y
oo! · Now the shep-herd gath-ers a gar-land,

In the wood a-new. Sing, cuck-oo! · Fill the world with
Buds of white and blue. Sing, cuck-oo! · Mel-o-dies of

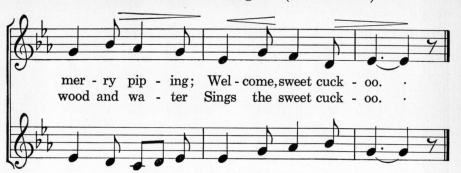

mer - ry pip - ing; Wel - come, sweet cuck - oo.
wood and wa - ter Sings the sweet cuck - oo.

Windmill Shadows

**English version by
Clara Louise Kessler**

Dutch Folk Song

Andante
mf

1. Breez - es blow, now high, now low, And
2. Daf - fo - dils with yel - low frills Are
3. Sharp they creak and shrill - y squeak, The

turn the wings of the wind-mill. Wing-like shad-ows, re -
kissed by slow-run-ning shad-ows. Gold - en tu - lips and
gi - ant wings of the wind-mill. On the gar - den, the

volv - ing shad-ows, Go sweep - ing o - ver the ground.
crim - son tu - lips Are tagged as wings turn a - round.
bright Dutch gar-den, Their shad-ows whirl with-out sound.

Heavy Load

Jane Beecham

Russian Folk Tune

1. An - na leads, and So - nia fol - lows
2. Moth - er rides with - out a fear of

aft - er, Draw - ing their heav - y
fall - ing; O - ver the snow are

load with cheer and laugh - ter. Moth-er car - ries the
hap - py voic - es call - ing. On they speed through the

ba - by tight; Furs are warm and blan - kets
win - ter wood, Through the froz - en win - ter

white. Oh, mer-ry, mer-ry! Tra la la la la
wood. Oh, mer-ry, mer-ry! Tra la la la la

la la la; Tra la la la la la la!
la la la; Tra la la la la la la!

The Art Extension Press, Inc.

Heavy Load

Painted by E. KAEMPFFER

The Traveler's Song

Christine Turner Curtis   Ruth McConn Spencer

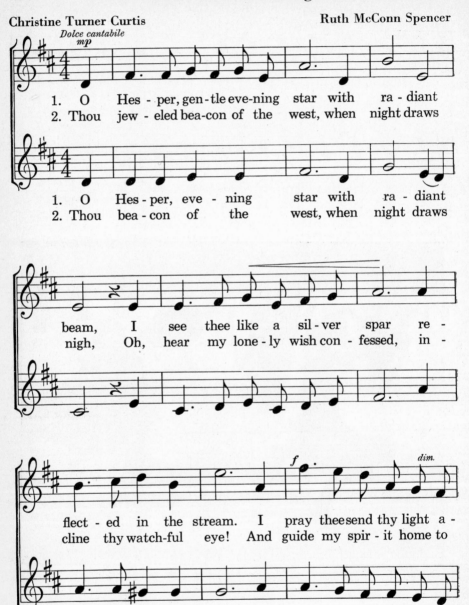

1. O Hes - per, gen - tle eve-ning star with   ra - diant
2. Thou jew - eled bea-con of the   west, when night draws

1. O Hes - per, eve - ning   star with   ra - diant
2. Thou bea - con of   the   west, when night draws

beam,   I   see   thee like a   sil - ver   spar   re -
nigh,   Oh, hear my lone - ly wish con - fessed,   in -

flect - ed   in the stream.   I   pray thee send thy light a -
cline thy watch-ful   eye! And guide my spir - it home to

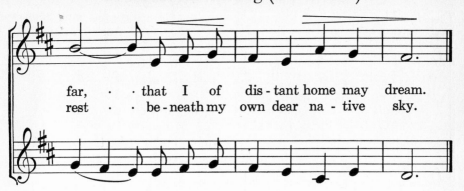

far, · · that I of dis - tant home may dream.
rest · · be - neath my own dear na - tive sky.

I Can

William Allen Butler

Newton Swift

Allegretto

"I can" is a work - er; He tills in the

fields, And digs from the earth All the wealth that it

yields. The hum of his spin - dles Be - gins with the

light; The fires of his forg-es Are blaz-ing all night.

5

126 The Dream

Translated by
Cecil Cowdrey

Austrian Folk Song

Sostenuto
mf

1. The mill - er's maid sat down to spin. A-
2. With - in that ring of mag - ic light Ap-
3. "Now tell me, pray, what make you there?" "I
4. The win - ter eve passed, cold and still: The

cross the floor the moon shone in; And
peared a fair and no - ble knight; In
spin a gar - ment rich and rare, A
moon had left the si - lent mill. The

in that qui - et beam She dreamed a won-drous dream.
plume and dou - blet gay He stood in fine ar - ray.
robe of pat - tern old, All bright with pearls and gold."
no - ble knight was gone; Yet still the maid dreamed on.

Marjorie Knapp

Irish Folk Tune

1. Come, my dears, and trip it light - ly, All with - out a
2. Come, sweet Peg - gy, No - ra, Mol - ly, Whirl and whirl a -

care; For the sun is shin - ing bright - ly And the
bout! Come now, Mi - chael, Col - in, Ker - ry, Dance with

flow'rs bloom fair. See the fields of em - 'rald
song and shout! Pur - ple hills and qui - et

green where lakes of gleam - ing sil - ver lie; Come, my
val - leys shine be - neath the hap - py sky; Come, my

dears, and trip it light - ly All with - out a care, For the
dears, and trip it light - ly All with - out a care, For the

sun is shin - ing bright - ly And the flow'rs bloom fair.
sun is shin - ing bright - ly And the flow'rs bloom fair.

The Broken Jar

Translated by
Hannah Bailey

Armenian Folk Song[1]

Grazioso
mf

1. Bright-ly on the foun-tain shone the eve-ning star; ·
2. Hear the wind blow wail-ing, hear the wind blow chill! ·

Came the love-ly maid-en with her emp-ty jar. ·
See the dark-ness drift-ing down the pur-ple hill! ·

Ling-'ring by the wa-ters, laugh-ing by the well;
Gone her sweet com-pan-ions, gone the eve-ning star;

[1] From the "Botsford Collection of Folk Songs," compiled and edited by Florence Hudson Botsford, Volume I, copyrighted 1922 and 1930 by G. Schirmer, Inc. Printed by permission.

From her head so black and beau-ti-ful slipped the jar and fell! ·
Sits the love-ly maid be-moan - ing her brok-en wa-ter jar! ·

Greeting

Heinrich Heine
Translated by
Cecil Cowdrey

Friedrich Frischenschlager[1]

1. Spring is in my heart to - day;
2. Haste to where in gar - den fair

Hap - py tunes are ring - ing. Out, you ti - ny
Vi - o - lets are sweet - er. If a rose you

song, a - way! Through sun - ny mead - ows wing - ing.
chance to spy, Pray tell her that I greet her.

[1] By permission of the original publishers, Universal Edition, Vienna; contained in " 12 Kinderlieder " by Frischenschlager.

The Cossack Riders

After the original by
Theresa L. Wilson

Russian Folk Song

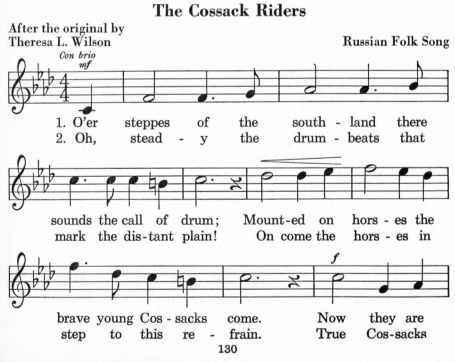

1. O'er steppes of the south - land there
2. Oh, stead - y the drum - beats that

sounds the call of drum; Mount-ed on hors - es the
mark the dis-tant plain! On come the hors - es in

brave young Cos - sacks come. Now they are
step to this re - frain. True Cos-sacks

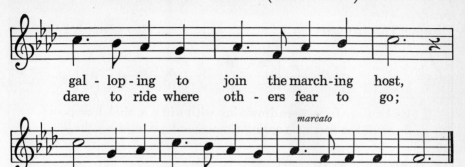

gal - lop - ing to join the march-ing host,
dare to ride where oth - ers fear to go;

marcato

Where floats the ban - ner that the Cos - sack loves the most.
Blue - coat - ed, whip in hand, they nev - er fear the foe.

Gala Day

Richard Gage

Italian Folk Tune

Vivace
mf

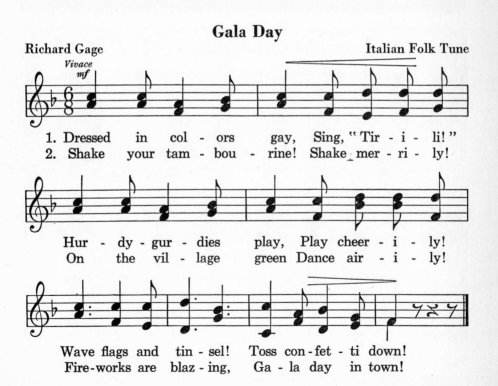

1. Dressed in col - ors gay, Sing, "Tir - i - li!"
2. Shake your tam - bou - rine! Shake mer - ri - ly!

Hur - dy - gur - dies play, Play cheer - i - ly!
On the vil - lage green Dance air - i - ly!

Wave flags and tin - sel! Toss con - fet - ti down!
Fire-works are blaz - ing, Ga - la day in town!

Seven Frogs

Translated by
Christine Turner Curtis

Dutch Folk Song

Giocoso

1. Sev - en frogs were drows-ing with - in a shal-low pool;
2. Soon the gen - tle spring-time came danc-ing down the hill;

They were near - ly froz - en, the day was ver - y cool.
All the frogs and peep - ers be - gan to pipe and trill,

Up spoke Fa - ther Frog, "Spring is on the way.
Croak - ing long and loud from the pools and bogs.

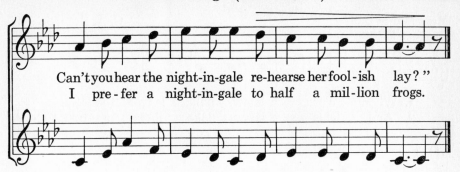

Can't you hear the night-in-gale re-hearse her fool-ish lay?"
I pre-fer a night-in-gale to half a mil-lion frogs.

English version by
Ethel Crowninshield

Drums

Polish Folk Song

Andantino
p

molto cres.

1. Hark, hear the mu-sic play! I hear it ev-'ry day.
2. May-be some hap-py day I'll have a drum to play.

f >

f >

Boom! the drum-mer goes, Boom! the rum-ble grows.
Boom! I want to go. Boom! I want to know

mf

Hear him com-ing, Hear him drum-ming!
Where to buy one, How to try one!

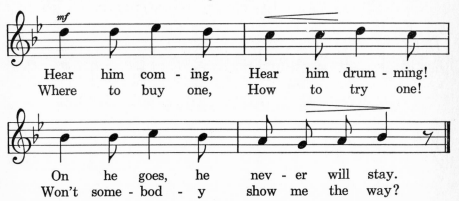

On he goes, he nev-er will stay.
Won't some-bod-y show me the way?

Snowflakes

Mary Mapes Dodge

G. A. Grant-Schaefer

Cantabile
mp

1. When - e'er · a snow - flake leaves the sky, It
2. And when · a snow - flake finds a tree, "Good

turns and turns to say, "Good-by! Good - by, dear clouds, so
day!" it says, "Good day to thee! Thou art so bare and

cool and gray!" Then light-ly trav-els on its way. ·
lone-ly, dear; I'll rest and call my com-rades here." ·

3. But when a snow-flake, brave and meek, Lights on · a ros - y

maid - en's cheek, It starts, "How warm and soft the

day! 'Tis sum-mer!" and it melts a - way. ·

Winter, You Must Go

Cecil Cowdrey

French Folk Tune

Larghetto

1. Win - ter, you must go! Your i - cy reign will
2. Win - ter, you must go! With seed a - stir on

soon be past. Spring's at the win-dow; She'll send you fly - ing
ev-'ry hand, Soft buds un - fold-ing To charm the wait-ing

fast. · Streams wake with rush and roar And, foam-ing, race a -
land. · Clouds wan - der o'er the blue A - bove the qui - et

Winter, You Must Go (*Continued*)

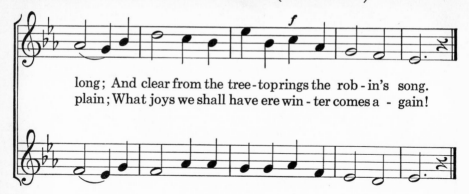

long; And clear from the tree-top rings the rob-in's song.
plain; What joys we shall have ere win-ter comes a - gain!

The Storm

Laura E. Richards

Frederick von Flotow

Energico

1. I won-der, I won-der what brings us the thun-der, That's
2. And now hear trees rus-tle with whis-tle and bus-tle; With

roll-ing from un-der that black and gloom-y cloud. The
toss-ing and tus-sle they bow be-neath the blast. And

light-ning comes flash-ing, the thun-der comes crash-ing, The
we too must hur-ry, must hur-ry and scur-ry, For

rain - drops come lash - ing; the wind is blow - ing loud.
moth - er will wor - ry if we don't scam - per fast.

Farmer Jack

Rose Fyleman   Bohemian-Czech Folk Tune

1. Home from the mar - ket comes Farm - er · · Jack; Show me now
2. Home from the mar - ket comes Farm - er · · Jack; Show me now

what you have brought me · back. Gowns of sat - in and
what you have brought me · back. Oak - en press - es and

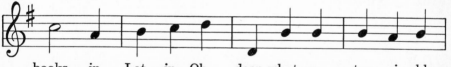

books in Lat - in. Oh, dear, what a ter - ri - ble
wool - en dress - es. Oh, my, what a ter - ri - ble

fool - ish · man! Take them all back just as quick as you · can.
clev - er · man! Bring them all in just as quick as you · can.

Carnival

English version by
Cecil Cowdrey

Italian Folk Song

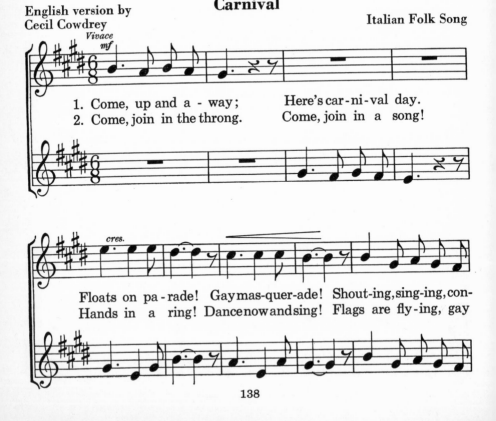

1. Come, up and a - way; Here's car-ni-val day.
2. Come, join in the throng. Come, join in a song!

Floats on pa - rade! Gay mas-quer-ade! Shout-ing, sing-ing, con-
Hands in a ring! Dance now and sing! Flags are fly-ing, gay

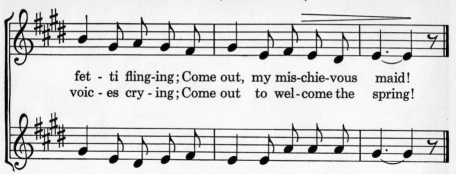

fet - ti fling-ing; Come out, my mis-chie-vous maid!
voic - es cry - ing; Come out to wel-come the spring!

Laughter

Elizabeth Garrett

English Folk Tune

Animato
mf

1. Oh, win - ter has gone and the spring is here.
2. Oh, learn how to laugh while the spring is here.

f

Heigh - o! heigh - o! When days are the bright-est and
Heigh - o! heigh - o! 'Twill save you from man - y a

Laughter (*Continued*)

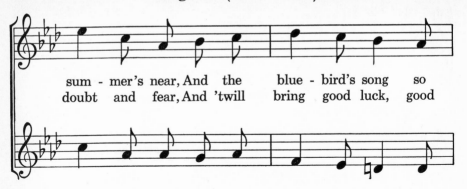

sum - mer's near, And the   blue - bird's song   so
doubt and fear, And 'twill   bring good luck,   good

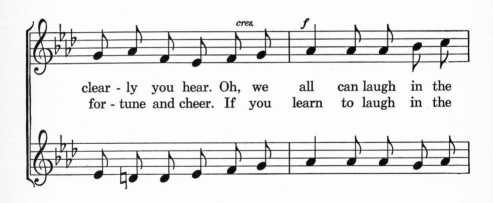

clear - ly you hear. Oh, we   all can laugh in the
for - tune and cheer. If you   learn to laugh in the

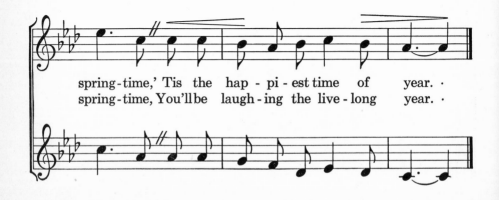

spring-time,' Tis the hap - pi - est time of   year. ·
spring-time, You'll be laugh - ing the live - long   year. ·

Ethel Crowninshield

1. Danc-ing in the glow of the sil - ver moon-light,
2. Lit - tle Span-ish maid, I can see her danc - ing!

Un - der-neath the branch of the al - mond tree,
Lit - tle Span-ish maid with a smil - ing face!

Glides a pret - ty maid-en in a black man - til - la,
High a-bove her head a ti - ny fan is wav - ing,

Air - y as a fair - y and as light and free.
As she twirls and as she whirls with per - fect grace.

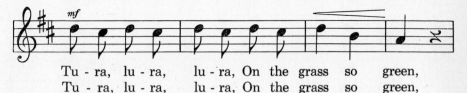

Tu - ra, lu - ra, lu - ra, On the grass so green,
Tu - ra, lu - ra, lu - ra, On the grass so green,

Danc-ing to the mu - sic of the tam - bou - rine.
Danc-ing to the mu - sic of the tam - bou - rine.

5

Herd in the Sunlight

Painted by ÉMILE CLAUS

Herd in the Sunlight

Hannah Bailey

French-Canadian Folk Tune

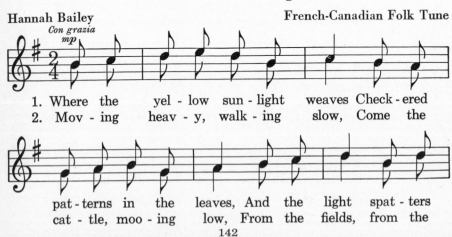

1. Where the yel - low sun - light weaves Check - ered
2. Mov - ing heav - y, walk - ing slow, Come the

pat - terns in the leaves, And the light spat - ters
cat - tle, moo - ing low, From the fields, from the

142

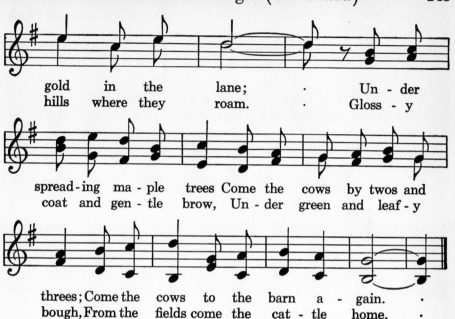

gold in the lane; · Un - der
hills where they roam. · Gloss - y

spread - ing ma - ple trees Come the cows by twos and
coat and gen - tle brow, Un - der green and leaf - y

threes; Come the cows to the barn a - gain. ·
bough, From the fields come the cat - tle home. ·

English version by
Christine Turner Curtis

Good-by

Filipino Folk Song

Leggiero
mp

1. The wind is in the co - coa palm, The tide runs high; · My
2. Oh, play your man-do-lin and sing A song for me · Be-

mf

ban - ca[1] waits up - on the sand; Good-by, Ra-quel, good-by. ·
fore I jour-ney far a - way A - cross the deep blue sea! ·

[1] A Filipino boat.

Spring Morning

Frances Ford

Christoph Wilibald Gluck

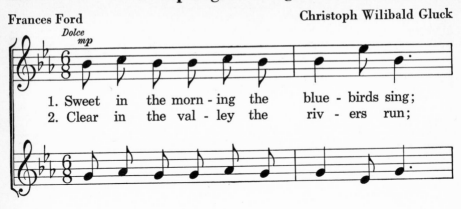

1. Sweet in the morn - ing the blue - birds sing;
2. Clear in the val - ley the riv - ers run;

Bright on the blos - som the dew - drops cling.
Cupped ev - 'ry cow - slip with yel - low sun.

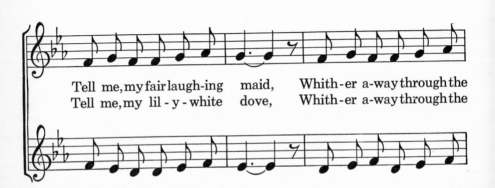

Tell me, my fair laugh-ing maid, Whith-er a-way through the
Tell me, my lil - y - white dove, Whith-er a-way through the

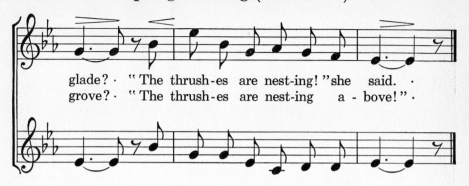

glade? · "The thrush-es are nest-ing!" she said. ·
grove? · "The thrush-es are nest-ing a - bove!" ·

The Wave

Translated by
Luther Wilde

Danish Folk Song

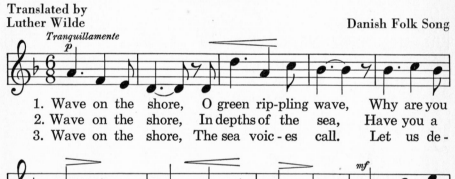

1. Wave on the shore, O green rip-pling wave, Why are you
2. Wave on the shore, In depths of the sea, Have you a
3. Wave on the shore, The sea voic-es call. Let us de-

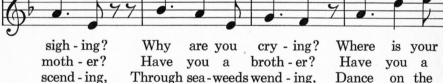

sigh - ing? Why are you cry - ing? Where is your
moth - er? Have you a broth - er? Have you a
scend - ing, Through sea-weeds wend - ing, Dance on the

home-land, and where is your cra-dle? Wave, rip-pling wave.
house where the sea flow'rs are climb-ing? Wave, rip-pling wave.
smooth, pearl-y floor of the o-cean, Wave, rip-pling wave.

The Golden Linnet

English version by
Hannah Bailey

Neapolitan Folk Song

1. One fair morn-ing the gen-tle Ma - ri - no · Caught a
2. When the lin - net was sent by his mas - ter · To the

lin - net that lived in the wood; And he called him his
house of a maid-en he knew, Through the trees he went

gold - en bam - bi - no,[1] · For the bird was de -
straight - er and fast - er · Than an ar - row could

vot - ed and good. He would fol - low his
speed through the blue. If he found that the

mas - ter when stroll - ing, He would fol - low his
maid - en was sleep - ing, He would light on a

mas - ter to prayer; · When the mu - sic was rip-pling and
rose-bush and stand; · But if she through her lat - tice was

[1] Italian word meaning "baby."

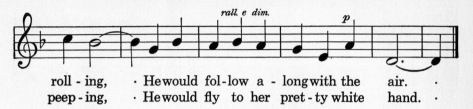

roll - ing, · He would fol-low a - long with the air. ·
peep - ing, · He would fly to her pret - ty white hand. ·

Night in the Garden

Marjorie Knapp   Franz Ries

1. The night has come with sil - ver stars a-glow, The
2. Oh, hap - py are these qui - et, drow - sy hours When

moon is full and bright. Through ma - ple boughs the
night is still and deep. We walk be - side the

cool - ing breez-es blow; They are the voice of night. They
si - lent, dream-ing flow'rs; Their watch the stars will keep When

sing fare-well to light, They sing fare-well to light.
gar - dens fall a - sleep, When gar - dens fall a - sleep.

Yesterday and Today

ROTE

Paraphrase by
Hope Ann Rhodes

English Folk Song

Ben marcato
mf

1. Oh, I've read tales of the long a - go, Of
2. If men of old could re - turn and see The

he - roes who were not a - fraid to face the foe;
things that ev - 'ry day are plain to you and me:

cres.

Of sail - ors who o'er seas did sail, And
How swift - ly through the sky we go; And

no, nev - er once did their cour - age fail!
hear all the news on the ra - di - o!

f

This was true long a - go, But
They would say, "I don't know, We

some - times I've asked if 'twere real - ly so.
hear this is true but it can't be so!"

English version by
Christine Turner Curtis

Swedish Folk Song

1. Loud sings the cuck - oo sweet;
2. Wel - come, sweet Gre - ta mine,

Loud rings the mu - sic down the street. Boom! goes the
Dressed in your ker - chief white and fine! Wel - come, gray

mer - ry drum. Come, one and all to the
Gun - nar old; Dance from your heart ev - 'ry

danc - ing, come! Dance win - ter snows a - way!
shiv - er cold! Sun - beams are danc - ing too;

Dance in the love - ly May! Sash - es are whirl - ing,
Eyes spar - kle brown and blue. Join in the danc - ing,

laugh - ter a-bounds; Gay - ly the mer - ry fid - dle sounds!
gay as a lark! Dance till the day - light turns to dark!

The Fisherman of Gloucester

Ethel Crowninshield   Traditional

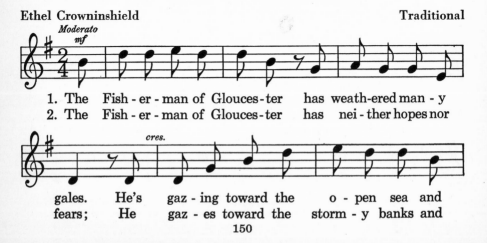

1. The Fish - er - man of Glouces - ter has weath-ered man - y
2. The Fish - er - man of Glouces - ter has nei - ther hopes nor

gales.   He's gaz - ing toward the   o - pen sea and
fears;   He gaz - es toward the storm - y banks and

look - ing for the sails Of the fish - ing boats of
out a - cross the years. For his heart is with the

Glouces - ter, from the port of miss - ing men; The
sail - ors in the port of miss - ing men; The

rall. e dim.

fish - ing boats of Glouces - ter that will nev - er come a - gain.
fish - ing boats of Glouces - ter that will nev - er come a - gain.

Song of the Flower Girl

Mary Smith   Anna von W. Grille

Sostenuto

1. Buy my ros - es, buy my ros - es, Buy my gold and
2. Buy my jon-quils, yel - low jon - quils, ros - es and my

crim - son ros - es. Spring is in their
yel - low jon - quils. Streets are bare, while

rall.

love - ly blos-soms; They will bring to you the spring-time.
in the wood-land Flow-ers bloom on ev - 'ry hill - side.

Robin Hood and Little John

Paraphrase by
Hope Ann Rhodes

English Folk Song

1. Come, Rob - in Hood! Come a - long, Lit - tle John! All the
2. Come, Rob - in Hood! Come a - long, Lit - tle John! Oh, you
3. Come, Rob - in Hood! Come a - long, Lit - tle John! To the

new green leaves will soon be show - ing.
both must come a - long to - geth - er.
fair your way you must be tak - ing.

See, on high all the geese are fly - ing by, For a -
From the sky as the geese are fly - ing by, They have
Think of that! With a feath - er in your hat, What a

way up north they now are go - ing!
dropped you each a shin - ing feath - er.
fine, fine show you'll both be mak - ing!

The Harper

Paraphrase by
Marjorie Knapp

Welsh Folk Song

1. O harp, thy gold - en sing - ing To my
2. If I should meet with sor - row, O my

spir - it glad - ness is bring - ing; My
harp, from thee I shall bor - row The

hap - py thoughts like birds go wing - ing When I can touch thy strings.
strength I need to greet the mor - row, What - ev - er grief it brings.

The Castle

Paraphrase by
Elizabeth Garrett

Welsh Folk Song

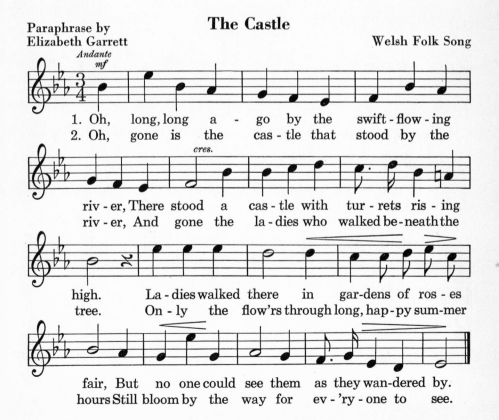

1. Oh, long, long a - go by the swift - flow - ing
2. Oh, gone is the cas - tle that stood by the

riv - er, There stood a cas - tle with tur - rets ris - ing
riv - er, And gone the la - dies who walked be - neath the

high. La - dies walked there in gar - dens of ros - es
tree. On - ly the flow'rs through long, hap - py sum - mer

fair, But no one could see them as they wan - dered by.
hours Still bloom by the way for ev - 'ry - one to see.

If

Mabel Livingstone

John Alden Carpenter

Oh, would not it be fun - ny, and would not peo - ple stare, · If feath - ers grew on chil - dren, and geese had gold - en

Oh, would not all the peo - ple stare If

hair!

geese had silk - y gold - en hair, had gold - en hair!

If ships sailed on the mead - ows, and hous - es on the

sea, And ev - 'ry - thing were dif - f'rent from

If (*Continued*)

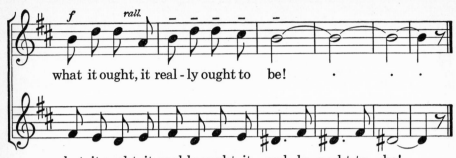

what it ought, it real - ly ought to be!

what it ought, it real-ly ought, it real - ly ought to be!

Gypsy Dancers

Translated by
Cecil Cowdrey

Spanish Folk Song

Con anima
mf

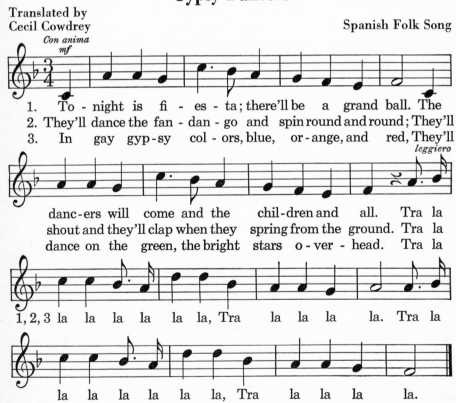

1. To - night is fi - es - ta; there'll be a grand ball. The
2. They'll dance the fan - dan - go and spin round and round; They'll
3. In gay gyp-sy col - ors, blue, or-ange, and red, They'll

leggiero

danc-ers will come and the chil-dren and all. Tra la
shout and they'll clap when they spring from the ground. Tra la
dance on the green, the bright stars o - ver - head. Tra la

1, 2, 3 la la la la la la, Tra la la la la. Tra la

la la la la la la, Tra la la la la.

English version by
Louise Ayres Garnett

Danish Folk Song

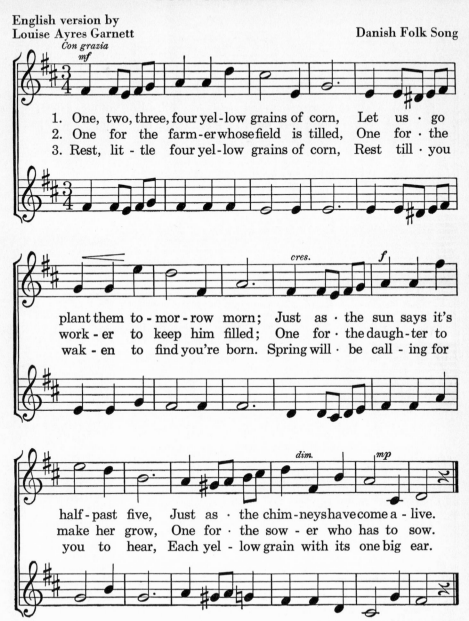

1. One, two, three, four yel-low grains of corn, Let us · go
2. One for the farm-er whose field is tilled, One for · the
3. Rest, lit - tle four yel-low grains of corn, Rest till · you

plant them to - mor - row morn; Just as · the sun says it's
work - er to keep him filled; One for · the daugh-ter to
wak - en to find you're born. Spring will · be call - ing for

half - past five, Just as · the chim-neys have come a - live.
make her grow, One for · the sow - er who has to sow.
you to hear, Each yel - low grain with its one big ear.

The Shepherdess

Carol Fuller

French Melody

Con grazia
mp

1. Lambs all the way are feed - ing, nib-bling young grass;
2. Past ros - es pink and glow - ing we take our way;

Here, where my flock I'm lead - ing, cloud shad-ows pass.
Where lil - y buds are grow - ing, lambs like to play.

cres.

Lambs white as fly - ing pet - als drift - ing a - long,
Out o - ver shin-ing mead-ows we wan - der free;

Up the hill you fol - low, down through leaf - y hol - low,
When the dusk is fall - ing, then I shall be call - ing,

When you hear my song.
" Chil - dren, come with me! "

The Shepherdess

The Art Extension Press, Inc.

Painted by the French artist HENRY LEROLLE. The
picture is now in the Luxembourg Museum, Paris

The Whistling Miller

Rose Fyleman

Welsh Folk Tune

Allegro
mf

1. Here come I, such a jol - ly mill - er,
2. Here come I, such a jol - ly mill - er,

Whis - tling for a breeze, oh! (WHISTLE) Soon it will bring me a
Ver - y smart and fine, oh! What shall I do with my

bag o' sil - ler, Pret - ty as you please, oh! (WHISTLE)
bag o' sil - ler, Now that it is mine, oh!

Breez - es make all my sails go round, And the
I'll go court - ing a bon - ny maid, And I'll

cres.

flour is speed - i - ly ground. So I whis - tle the
whis - tle if I'm a - fraid. Say she no, then, or

whole long day And keep care a - way.
say she yes, I'll whis - tle no less.

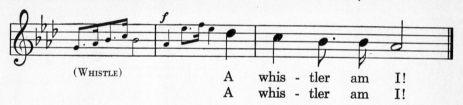

(WHISTLE)

A whis - tler am I!
A whis - tler am I!

English version by
Marjorie Knapp

For Music

Robert Franz

Andante molto sostenuto

1. When the morn-ing's break-ing, ros - y col - ors mak - ing,
2. Still by songs at - tend - ed comes the noon-time splen - did,

Then, with mu-sic wak - ing, we are greet-ing the light.
With the sun as - cend - ed to its ra - di - ant height.

3. Aft - er sun - set gleam - ing, when the stars are

beam - ing, Mu - sic brings sweet dream - ing,

Mu-sic, mu-sic through the day and through the night.

5

By the Volga

English version by
Louise Ayres Garnett

Russian Folk Song

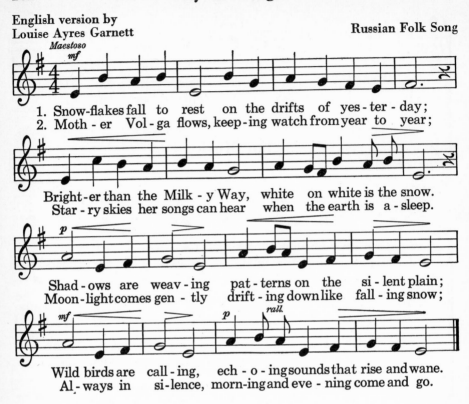

1. Snow-flakes fall to rest on the drifts of yes-ter-day;
2. Moth-er Vol-ga flows, keep-ing watch from year to year;

Bright-er than the Milk-y Way, white on white is the snow.
Star-ry skies her songs can hear when the earth is a-sleep.

Shad-ows are weav-ing pat-terns on the si-lent plain;
Moon-light comes gen-tly drift-ing down like fall-ing snow;

Wild birds are call-ing, ech-o-ing sounds that rise and wane.
Al-ways in si-lence, morn-ing and eve-ning come and go.

Hymn to Spring

Richard Gage

Christoph Wilibald Gluck

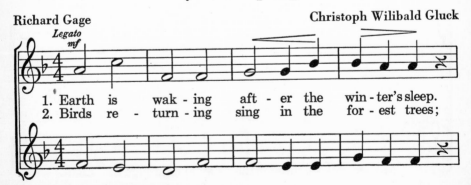

1. Earth is wak-ing aft-er the win-ter's sleep.
2. Birds re-turn-ing sing in the for-est trees;

Raise your voic - es in joy and in praise!
Flow'rs spring up where the white snow has lain.

Riv - ers ice - bound now are flow - ing, While
Come, re - joice with songs and danc - ing! For

sun - shine falls warm through the long, gen - tle days.
earth is a - wake and the spring comes a - gain.

When Spring Sends the Flowers

English version by
Carol Fuller

Czech Folk Song

1. Look, how the fields are chang-ing! Col-ors bright I see.
2. Come, let us give them greet-ing! Glad-ly march and sing.

Love from the skies ar-rang-ing Flow-ers for you and me.
Buds we are now en-treat-ing Gen-er-ous bloom to bring.

Shin - ing lil - ies bless their Giv - er,
Flow'r - bells ring - ing join in prais - es;

Hare - bells blue as rush - ing riv - er,
We are friends of pinks and dai - sies.

Per-fume and bows ex-chang-ing, Nod-ding sweet and free.
Joy - ful - ly all are meet-ing, Thank-ing God for Spring!

Mabel Livingstone

Victor Young

1. A June bug nev - er seems to know Ex -
2. He drops right down up - on our heads, He
3. He thinks the June days are so bright. He

act - ly where he wants to go; He
flops in - to the flow - er beds, And
gets all diz - zy with de - light, As

does - n't seem to mind the sun Or
there he kicks his ti - ny feet And
up - side down and down - side up, He

me or you or an - y - one. "Sz - z, sz - z,
hums a - bout the sum - mer heat. "Sz - z, sz - z,
sings to rose and but - ter - cup. "Sz - z, sz - z,

sz-z," he sings, "Sz-z, sz-z, sz - z," he sings, "Sz-z, sz-z, sz - z."
sz-z," he sings, "Sz-z, sz-z, sz - z," he sings, "Sz-z, sz-z, sz - z."
sz-z," he sings, "Sz-z, sz-z, sz - z," he sings, "Sz-z, sz-z, sz - z."

The Minuet

Christine Turner Curtis

Jacques Offenbach

1. When it is cold win - ter time, To the
2. Put on a pink sat - in gown With the
3. Put on a blue sat - in coat With a

at - tic we climb, And we o - pen a
lace float - ing down, And the rib - bons that
ruff at the throat, And the vest with the

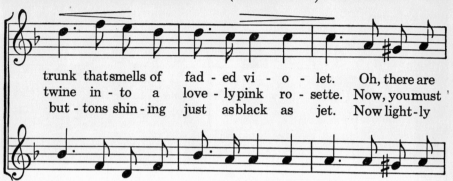

trunk that smells of fad - ed vi - o - let. Oh, there are
twine in - to a love - ly pink ro - sette. Now, you must '
but - tons shin - ing just as black as jet. Now light - ly

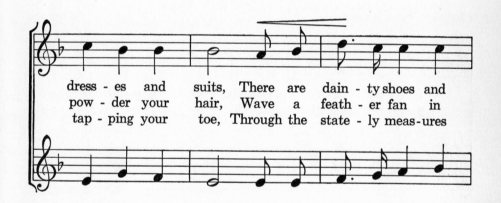

dress - es and suits, There are dain - ty shoes and
pow - der your hair, Wave a feath - er fan in
tap - ping your toe, Through the state - ly meas - ures

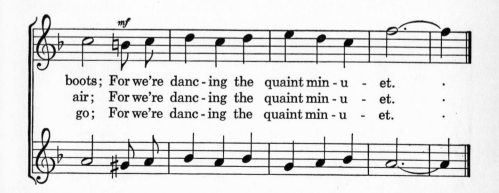

boots; For we're danc - ing the quaint min - u - et.
air; For we're danc - ing the quaint min - u - et.
go; For we're danc - ing the quaint min - u - et.

Spring Song

Rose Fyleman

Norwegian Folk Tune

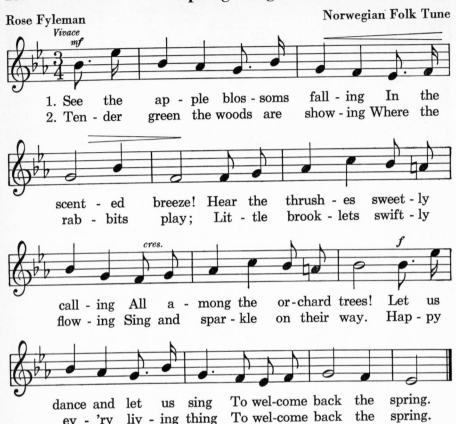

1. See the ap - ple blos - soms fall - ing In the
2. Ten - der green the woods are show - ing Where the

scent - ed breeze! Hear the thrush - es sweet - ly
rab - bits play; Lit - tle brook - lets swift - ly

call - ing All a - mong the or - chard trees! Let us
flow - ing Sing and spar - kle on their way. Hap - py

dance and let us sing To wel-come back the spring.
ev - 'ry liv - ing thing To wel-come back the spring.

The Friendly Star

After the original by
Carol Fuller

Polish Folk Song

1. Man - y stars that shine in splen - dor
2. Does your gleam - ing teach me dream - ing,

High   a - loft   I   see.   One with sil - ver
Friend - ly star   so   kind?   Morn - ing glo - ries,

light   so ten - der Watch - es o - ver   me.
fair - y sto - ries,   In my sleep I   find.

Star   a - bove me,   calm - ly wend - ing
Lamp   of Heav'n, in   beau - ty burn - ing,

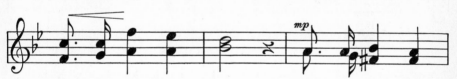

Through the deeps of   night,   Down the pur - ple
Send your bright - est beams.   Ev - 'ry night in

skies de - scend - ing, Shine for my de - light.
joy re - turn - ing,   Bring me rain - bow dreams!

A Song of Summer

Author unknown

Jacques Wolfe

A cuck-oo sat on a tree and sang,

"Sum-mer is a-com-ing, Sum-mer is a-com-ing."

And a bee crept out of the hive and be-gan

La-zy, la-zy hum-ming, La-zy, la-zy hum-ming.

The frogs, from out of the rush-es and reeds,

In-to the wa-ter went splash-ing; And the

drag - on fly, with his bod - y of green,

Through the flags went flash - ing, flash - ing. For

sum - mer had come, and the cuck - oo sang His

song through wood-land and hol - low, Wood - land and

hol - low; · · "The sum-mer is come! If you

don't be - lieve me, You have on - ly to ask the

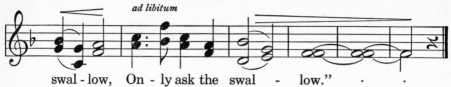

swal - low, On - ly ask the swal - low." . .

Moon-talk

Mary C. Gleitz

Mary B. Black

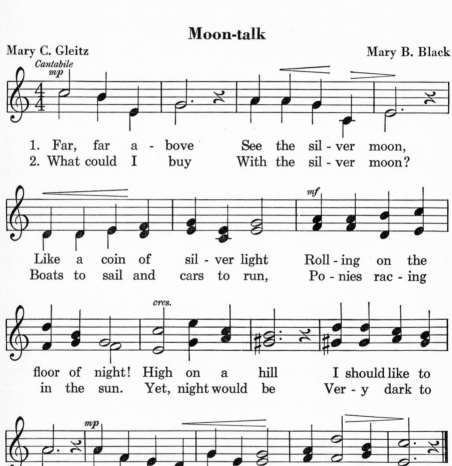

1. Far, far a - bove See the sil - ver moon,
2. What could I buy With the sil - ver moon?

Like a coin of sil - ver light Roll - ing on the
Boats to sail and cars to run, Po - nies rac - ing

floor of night! High on a hill I should like to
in the sun. Yet, night would be Ver - y dark to

stand; There I'd catch and hold the moon Close in my hand.
me; I had bet - ter leave the moon Where it should be!

ROTE

Clara Edwards

Clara Edwards

1. "Too wit, too wit, too wit, too wee," A
2. Bring out your bag of seeds and rake, Bring

brown bird sang to me, "Get up and come out
out your spade and hoe! A love - ly gar - den

quick - ly, There's so much here to see. The
mak - ing Where mar - i - golds may grow. Then

wil - low hedge is blos - som - ing, There
you can rest be - side the brook Where

I can sit and swing. The cher - ry tree is
cool green moss - es cling, While I sit on the

white with bloom, The rea - son, it is spring!
near - est branch. ' 'Tis May - time,' hear me sing!"

Saint Marie

English version by
Ethel Crowninshield

French-Canadian Folk Song

1. Down the streams All the swift ca - noes glide
2. Sing your songs While the sum - mer - time is
3. Back a - gain To the fro - zen North you'll

on. All the hunt - ers now are sing - ing; Rich
here. Soon the north wind will be blow - ing, And
go; But be - side the glow - ing em - ber, Each

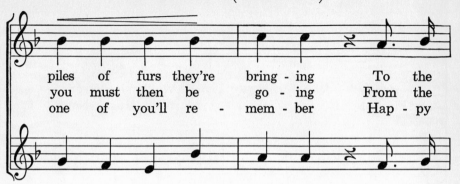

piles of furs they're bring-ing To the
you must then be go-ing From the
one of you'll re-mem-ber Hap-py

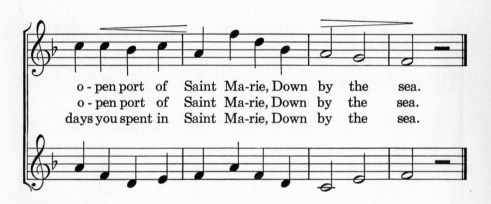

o-pen port of Saint Ma-rie, Down by the sea.
o-pen port of Saint Ma-rie, Down by the sea.
days you spent in Saint Ma-rie, Down by the sea.

A Merry Song

Marjorie Knapp

Franz Josef Haydn

Animato
f

1. Hi ho, hi ho! Sing-ing we will go. Hi ho,
2. Hi ho, hi ho! Laugh-ing we will go. Hi ho,

A Merry Song (*Continued*)

hi ho!   Jol - ly songs we know. We'll   sing and dance, we'll
hi ho!   Eyes are all   a - glow. We'll laugh when day is

skip   and we'll run; We'll   sing   with rain, we'll
sun - ny and bright; We'll   laugh   when shad - ows

sing with the sun. Ding dong, sing song! Sing - ing we will go.
fall with the night. Ding dong, sing song! Laugh-ing we will go.

Pietro's Hat

After the original by
Clara Louise Kessler

Italian Folk Song

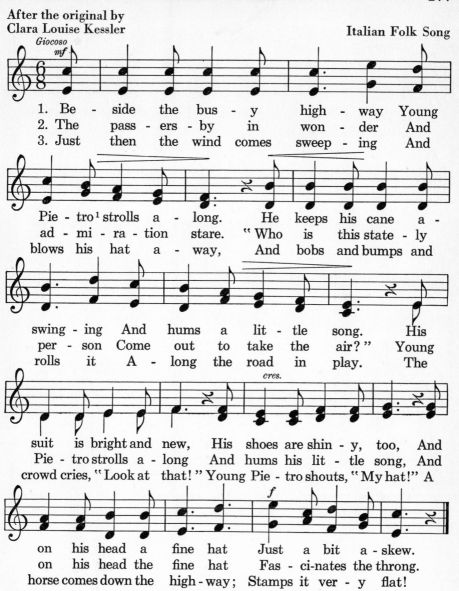

Giocoso
mf

1. Be - side the bus - y high - way Young
2. The pass - ers - by in won - der And
3. Just then the wind comes sweep - ing And

Pie - tro¹ strolls a - long. He keeps his cane a -
ad - mi - ra - tion stare. "Who is this state - ly
blows his hat a - way, And bobs and bumps and

swing - ing And hums a lit - tle song. His
per - son Come out to take the air?" Young
rolls it A - long the road in play. The

cres.

suit is bright and new, His shoes are shin - y, too, And
Pie - tro strolls a - long And hums his lit - tle song, And
crowd cries, "Look at that!" Young Pie - tro shouts, "My hat!" A

f

on his head a fine hat Just a bit a - skew.
on his head the fine hat Fas - ci - nates the throng.
horse comes down the high - way; Stamps it ver - y flat!

¹ Pronounced "pyā′tro."

5

Paul and the Chickens

Translated by
Cecil Cowdrey

Norwegian Folk Song

1. Free on the hill - side the brown chick-ens wan - dered;
2. Paul rushed a - way to the green slop - ing hill - side;

Paul drove them gen - tly the green hill a - long.
Far through the gloam - ing he fol - lowed them on.

Sud - den he heard such a cack - ling and call - ing,
Night com - ing down and the day al - most o - ver,

Paul in a mo - ment knew some - thing was wrong.
Paul found his chick - ens; a - las, one was gone!

"Cluck - y cluck," the poor chick - ens were cry - ing;
Rey - nard fled with his red tail a - fly - ing.

"Cluck - y cluck." Sad - ly Paul hur - ried sigh - ing,
Rey - nard fled; sad - ly Paul wan-dered cry - ing,

"Rey - nard the fox must be out on their trail,
Fast fell his tears on his long home-ward way;

Rey - nard the fox with his long bush - y tail."
"Oh, woe is me! What a sad sum-mer day!"

Frederick H. Martens **I Wonder** German Folk Tune

Cantabile
mp

1. There shines a star in heav'n at night,
2. I won - der wheth - er on that star,

High, high o - ver - head. I see the stead - y
High, high shin - ing free, Some oth - er hap - py

gold - en · light Glim - mer and spread
peo - ple · are, Peo - ple like me,

when I'm in bed. Oh, · strange and love - ly · sight!
peo - ple who see Our · earth be - low them far.

In the Queen's Garden

ROTE

Carol Fuller

Wolfgang Amadeus Mozart

Grazioso
mp

1. Flow - ers sleep - ing, foun - tains leap - ing,
2. Now is dawn - ing pink of morn - ing;

Moon-light can tell us of scenes long a - go:
Night-time has gone from the gar - den and park;

cres.

Court of France in lace and sat - in,
Danc - ers glim - mer ev - er dim - mer;

mf

Danc - ing a min - u - et, state - ly and slow.
Then they have van-ished and fol - lowed the dark.

p

Jew - els flash - ing, foun - tain splash - ing,
All grows light - er, sun is bright - er,

Mar - ble fig - ures gleam through the trees.
Shad - ows fade, and dreams dis - ap - pear;

Mu - sic play - ing, some - one say - ing,
Wa - ter fall - ing, birds are call - ing,

" Prin - cess, so beau - ti - ful, sing to me, please.
" Where is our prin - cess who sang to us here?

While stars shine o - ver you, sing to me, please! "
Long years have passed since she sang to us here."

Song of the Flowers

Mary C. Gleitz

French Folk Tune

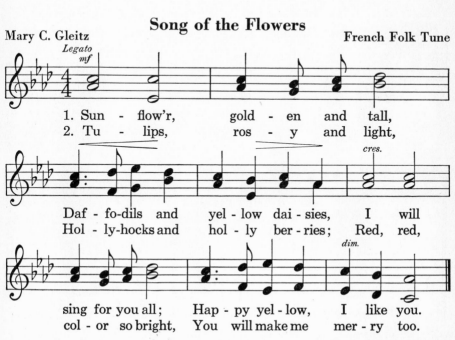

1. Sun - flow'r, gold - en and tall,
2. Tu - lips, ros - y and light,

Daf - fo-dils and yel - low dai - sies, I will
Hol - ly-hocks and hol - ly ber - ries; Red, red,

sing for you all; Hap - py yel - low, I like you.
col - or so bright, You will make me mer - ry too.

In the Plaza

English version by
Christine Turner Curtis

Mexican Folk Song

Andante cantabile

1. Sway-ing · be-neath the man-goes, Danc-ers · are weav-ing
2. Crim-son, · in gar-dens hill-y, Blos-soms · the ti-ger

tan-gos; Soft-ly · the lutes are sigh-ing, · And o-ver-
lil-y. Pi-geons · will soon be wing-ing; · The lit-tle

head with shin-ing stars the sky is sown. · Red heels are
goats will soon be skip-ping in the dawn. · The palm trees

tap-ping, · black eyes are snap-ping; · On dress-es silk-y ·
shiv-er, · the ban-jos quiv-er. · Gar-de-nias cream-y ·

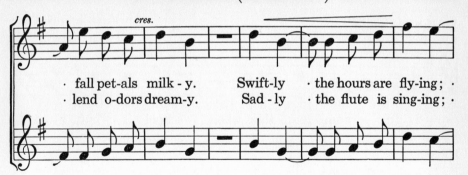

cres.

fall pet-als milk - y.   Swift-ly   the hours are fly-ing;
lend o-dors dream-y.   Sad - ly   the flute is sing-ing;

Too soon the balm-y night of   sum-mer will be   flown.
Too soon the love-ly night of   sum-mer will be   gone.

The Happiest Season

Clara Louise Kessler

English Folk Tune

1. It's mar - bles in the sum - mer - time, And
2. In sum - mer - time when school is out, From

bon - fires in the fall. It's skat - ing in the
ear - ly morn till night We play and run and

win - ter - time, And in the spring it's
loud - ly shout, And throw our bats and

base - ball time. Now which one of these sea - sons Is
balls a - bout. Oh, sum - mer is the best time, With

quite the best of all: Hap - py spring - time,
flow - ers gay and bright. Brooks are flow - ing,

play or school time, Sum - mer, win - ter, fall? ·
green things grow - ing; What a pleas - ant sight! ·

Ship in the Harbor

English version by
Hope Ann Rhodes

Japanese Folk Song

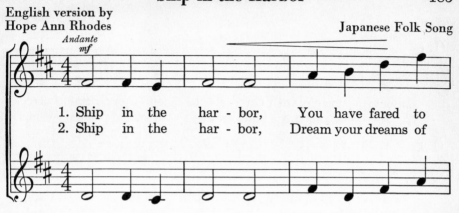

1. Ship in the har - bor, You have fared to
2. Ship in the har - bor, Dream your dreams of

ports a - far; Winds have blown you,
oth - er days, Gone for - ev - er.

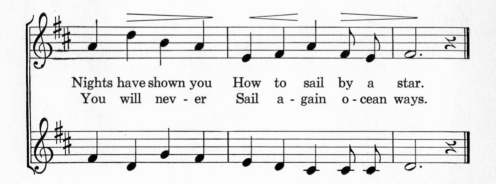

Nights have shown you How to sail by a star.
You will nev - er Sail a - gain o - cean ways.

A Smile

Ethel Crowninshield

Newton Swift

Con grazia

1. Some peo - ple with nev - er a pen - ny to spend Are
2. A smile and a kind-ness will al - ways re - main When

rich - er than those with gold; · They
all of your gold is spent; · You

al - ways have plen - ty and some-thing to lend That
nev - er, no nev - er can spend them in vain, No

ne'er can be bought nor sold. · A smile, I am told, can be
mat - ter how far you're sent. · Though o - ver the world you may

bought with a smile, And kind - ness is giv - en
trav - el some day, You al - ways will find it's

free; · You may fill up your pock - ets in
true, · If you smile at your friends all a -

an - y style, But those are the rich - es for me!
long the way, They'll al - ways be smil-ing at you.

A Song of Farewell

Translated by
Cecil Cowdrey

Hungarian Folk Song

Sostenuto

1. Si - lent, si - lent, falls the soft dew.
2. Si - lent, si - lent, lies the wide plain.

Sad the part - ing, com-rades, for you!
Dark - ly, dark - ly, falls the thick rain.

poco più moto

Fare thee well, dear land! I'm leav-ing for a strange shore.
Through the field my good horse pac-es, past the lone dell.

mf

Shall I then, in ex - ile griev-ing, See thee no more?
One last look, be - lov-ed plac - es. Home-land, fare - well!

A Funny Story

Margaret Johnson

Richmond K. Fletcher

1. When Tom - my Brown went out to sail, He
2. This fish was weep - ing sore with woe; To
3. He clapped his lit - tle fins for glee That

leaned too far a - cross the rail And
school he could not hope to go, Be -
so much bet - ter he could see, And

dropped his pre - cious glass - es! And dropped his pre - cious
cause he was near - sight - ed, Be - cause he was near-
now ful - filled his wish - es, And now ful - filled his

glass - es! He saw them sink but nev - er knew A
sight - ed. When look - ing up through tears that rose, He
wish - es. His heart is light, yes light and gay; For

fish was ly - ing 'neath the blue Where wave the long sea
caught those glass - es on his nose, And was - n't he de -
off he went that ver - y day And joined a school of

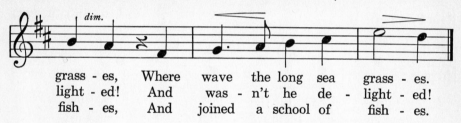

grass - es, Where wave the long sea grass - es.
light - ed! And was - n't he de - light - ed!
fish - es, And joined a school of fish - es.

Mary C. Gleitz **Circus Parade** Theo Halle

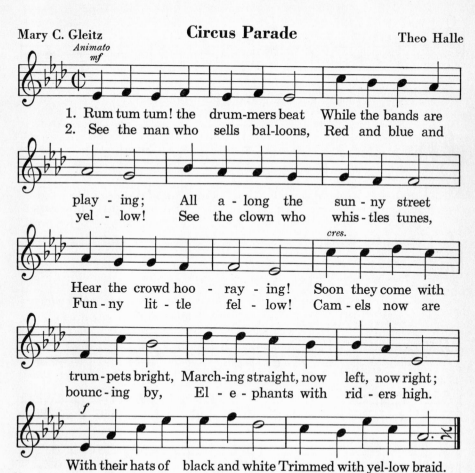

1. Rum tum tum! the drum-mers beat While the bands are
2. See the man who sells bal-loons, Red and blue and

play - ing; All a - long the sun - ny street
yel - low! See the clown who whis - tles tunes,

Hear the crowd hoo - ray - ing! Soon they come with
Fun - ny lit - tle fel - low! Cam - els now are

trum-pets bright, March-ing straight, now left, now right;
bounc - ing by, El - e - phants with rid - ers high.

With their hats of black and white Trimmed with yel-low braid.
Peo - ple clap their hands and cry, "What a grand pa-rade!"

A Song of the Country

Rose Fyleman

Welsh Folk Tune

1. Oh, sweet is the lark as I fol-low the
2. They say there are won-der-ful cit-ies a-

plow! And sweet is the rob-in up-on the green
far, Where gar-dens and foun-tains and ter-rac-es

bough! And dear is the sun-light and dear is the
are. They say there are pal-ac-es shin-ing with

dew, And clouds that go sail-ing a-cross the wide
gold, With stat-ues and jew-els and treas-ures un-

blue! But sweet-est of all are the bells that I hear When
told. But how could their beau-ties be fair-er than these, Than

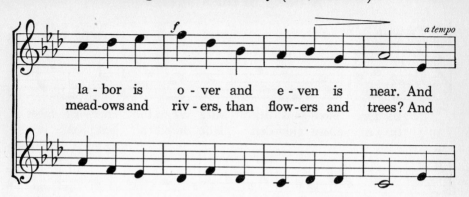

la - bor is o - ver and e - ven is near. And
mead-ows and riv - ers, than flow-ers and trees? And

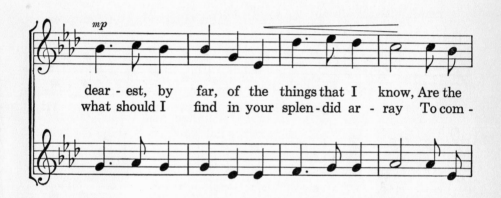

dear - est, by far, of the things that I know, Are the
what should I find in your splen-did ar - ray To com -

smiles that a - wait me as home-ward I go.
pare with my wel - come at close of the day?

In the Blossoming May

**English version by
Hannah Bailey**

Argentine Folk Song

Dolce espressivo
mp

In the blos-som-ing May When the cher-ry buds
In a green gar-den glade Stood a beau-ti-ful

sway, I was rid-ing my horse through the lane;
maid, With the dream-y-eyed glanc-es of

cres.

Spain. · She gath-ered a spic-y car-na-tion; · She
give you a spic-y car-na-tion, · I'll

f

gath-ered a sweet-scent-ed rose; · · "Dear
give you a rose-bud to-day, · · If

dim.

maid-en," I said, "With a rose-bud of red, You could
you'll prom-ise me ev-er kind-ly to be, Ev-er

con-quer my heart, if you chose." · "I'll
gra-cious as gar-dens in May." ·

Mary Smith

Jan Sibelius

1. Bright as gold the prim - rose bud - ded
2. Long, too long did win - ter chain her
3. Bright as gold the prim - rose bud - ded

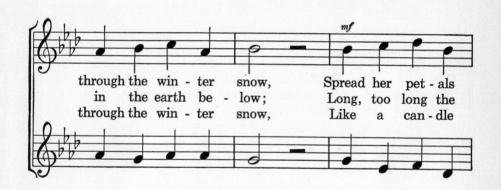

through the win - ter snow, Spread her pet - als
in the earth be - low; Long, too long the
through the win - ter snow, Like a can - dle

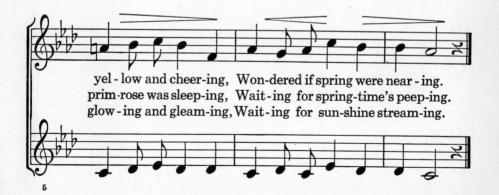

yel - low and cheer-ing, Won-dered if spring were near - ing.
prim-rose was sleep-ing, Wait-ing for spring-time's peep-ing.
glow - ing and gleam-ing, Wait-ing for sun-shine stream-ing.

Lullaby

English version by
Susanna Myers

Yugoslavian Folk Song

1. Soft - ly, soft - ly, sing sweet lull-a - by, Croon-ing, croon-ing
2. Soft - ly, soft - ly, sing sweet lull-a - by, Croon-ing, croon-ing

lull - a - by, lull - a - by. Dream-land o - pens fair - y
lull - a - by, lull - a - by. En - ter, all ye drow - sy

por - tals, Calls with - in all sleep-ing mor - tals.
mor - tals; En - ter dream-land's fair - y por - tals.

A Make-Believe Trip

Rebecca B. Foresman

English Folk Tune

1. Oh   come! Let's play that we're on   the   sea, And the
2. Oh   come! Let's play that our crew is   wise, That they

waves   are   high   as waves can   be;   But we
un - der - stand the sea and   skies.   They are

need   not   fear e'en the   ver - y strong-est gale, For we're
ver - y   jol - ly,   as   sail - ors ought to   be;   And we

just   pre - tend - ing we have   masts and   sail; And   a
don't need mon - ey   on this   trip, you   see,   For   a

make - be - lieve   sail - or   can't   fail.
make - be - lieve   trip should be   free.

America

S. F. Smith

Henry Carey

1. My coun - try! 'tis of thee, Sweet land of
2. My na - tive coun - try, thee — Land of the
3. Let mu - sic swell the breeze, And ring from
4. Our fa - thers' God! to Thee, Au - thor of

lib - er - ty, Of thee I sing; Land where my
no - ble free, Thy name I love; I love thy
all the trees Sweet free-dom's song; Let mor - tal
lib - er - ty, To Thee we sing; Long may our

fa - thers died! Land of the Pil - grims' pride!
rocks and rills, Thy woods and tem - pled hills;
tongues a - wake, Let all that breathe par - take,
land be bright With free - dom's ho - ly light!

From ev - 'ry moun - tain side Let · free - dom ring!
My heart with rap - ture thrills Like that a - bove.
Let rocks their si - lence break, The sound pro - long.
Pro - tect us by Thy might, Great God, our King!

Francis Scott Key   John Stafford Smith

Con spirito

1. Oh, · say! can you see, · by the dawn's ear - ly light, What so
2. On the shore, dim - ly seen thro' the mists of the deep, Where the
3. Oh, · thus be it ev - er when free - men shall stand Be -

proud - ly we hailed at the twi - light's last gleam - ing, Whose broad
foe's haugh-ty host in dread si - lence re - pos - es, What is
tween their loved homes and the war's des - o - la - tion! Blest with

stripes and bright stars, thro' the per - il - ous fight, O'er the ram-parts we
that which the breeze, o'er the tow - er - ing steep, As it fit - ful - ly
vic - t'ry and peace, may the Heav'n-res-cued land Praise the Pow'r that hath

watch'd were so gal - lant - ly stream-ing? And the rock - ets' red glare,
blows, half con-ceals, half dis - clos - es? Now it catch - es the gleam
made and pre-served us a na - tion! Then con-quer we must,

the bombs burst-ing in air, Gave proof thro' the night that our
of the morn-ing's first beam, In full glo - ry re - flect-ed, now ·
when our cause it is just, And · this be our mot - to: "In · ·

CHORUS

flag was still there. Oh, · say, does that Star-span-gled Ban-ner yet
shines on the stream. 'Tis the Star-span-gled Ban-ner: oh, long may it
God is our trust!" And the Star-span-gled Ban-ner in tri-umph shall

wave · O'er the land · · of the free and the home of the brave!

Father, Lead Me Day by Day

John P. Hopps

Georg C. Strattner

Andante
mf

1. Fa-ther, lead me day by day, Ev-er in Thine own sweet way;
2. When in dan-ger, make me brave, Make me know that Thou canst save;
3. When I'm tempt-ed to do wrong, Make me stead-fast, wise, and strong;

Teach me to be pure and true, Show me what I ought to do.
Keep me safe by Thy dear side; Let me in Thy love a-bide.
And when all a-lone I stand, Shield me with Thy might-y hand.

The Three Kings

Translated

French Folk Song

Alla marcia
mf

Late at night, up-on the great high-way, I saw three kings of the East come

rid-ing; In the sky there shone a star-ry ray To guide these

Fine mp

kings up-on their ea-ger way. While no-ble court-iers went on be-

fore, And gold and price-less treas-ure bore, The slaves and

war-riors with shield and spear Dis-pelled the dan-gers that hov-ered near.

A Frog He Would A-Wooing Go

Traditional   *Con spirito*   **English Folk Song**

1. A Frog he would a - woo - ing go, Heigh - ho, says Ro-ley. A
2. He bri - dled him a big black snail, Heigh - ho, says Ro-ley. He

Frog he would a - woo - ing go Wheth-er his moth-er would
bri - dled him a big black snail, Sad - dled and rode it 'twixt

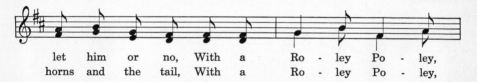

let him or no, With a Ro - ley Po - ley,
horns and the tail, With a Ro - ley Po - ley,

Gam-mon and Spin-ach, Heigh - ho, says An - tho - ny Ro - ley.
Gam-mon and Spin-ach, Heigh - ho, says An - tho - ny Ro - ley.

3. "Pray, Mistress Mouse are you within?"
"Yes, sir, for here I am sitting to spin."

4. While she was sitting there to spin,
Cat and her kittens came tumbling right in.

5. So Mister Frog in terrible fright
Took up his hat and he wished them good night.

6. As he was passing o'er the brook,
Lily-White Duck came and gobbled him up.

God of the Earth, the Sky, the Sea

Samuel Longfellow

Henry F. Hemy

Largo

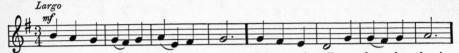

1. God of the earth, the sky, the sea! Mak-er of all a-bove, be-low!
2. Thy love is in · the sun-shine's glow, Thy life is in the quick-'ning air;
3. We feel Thy calm at eve-ning's hour, Thy gran-deur in the march of night;

Cre-a-tion lives and moves in Thee, Thy pres-ent life through all · doth flow.
When light-nings flash and storm-winds blow, There is Thy power; Thy law is there.
And, when Thy morn-ing breaks in power, We hear Thy word, 'Let there be light.'

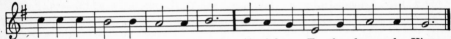

1, 2, 3. We give Thee thanks, Thy name we sing, Al-might-y Fa-ther, heaven-ly King.

The Little Sandman

Translated

Johannes Brahms

Andante dolce

p

1. The flow'r-ets all sleep sound-ly, Be-neath the moon's bright ray; They
2. The birds that sang so sweet-ly When noon-day sun rose high, With-
3. Now see, the lit-tle sand-man At the win-dow shows his head, And

mp

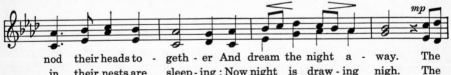

nod their heads to-geth-er And dream the night a-way. The
in their nests are sleep-ing: Now night is draw-ing nigh. The
looks for all good chil-dren Who ought to be · in bed; And

bud-ding trees wave to and fro, And mur-mur soft and low.
crick-et, as it moves a-long, A-lone gives forth its song.
as each wea-ry pet he spies, Throws sand in-to its eyes.

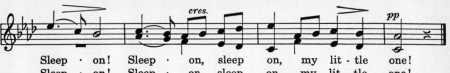

Sleep · on! Sleep · on, sleep on, my lit - tle one!
Sleep · on! Sleep · on, sleep on, my lit - tle one!
Sleep · on! Sleep · on, sleep on, my lit - tle one!

I Heard the Bells on Christmas Day

Henry W. Longfellow   J. Baptiste Calkin

Con spirito

1. I heard the bells on Christ-mas Day Their old fa - mil - iar car - ols play,
2. And thought how, as the day had come, The bel - fries of all Chris-ten-dom
3. Till, ring - ing, sing-ing on its way, The world re-volved from night to day,
4. Then pealed the bells more loud and deep : "God is not dead, nor doth He sleep!

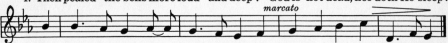

And wild and sweet the words re-peat Of peace on earth, good-will to men.
Had rolled a - long the un - brok - en song Of peace on earth, good-will to men.
A voice, a chime, a · chant sub-lime Of peace on earth, good-will to men.
The wrong shall fail, the right pre-vail, With peace on earth, good-will to men."

Hear Us, Our Father

Anonymous   Frederick C. Maker

Sostenuto

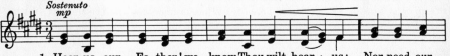

1. Hear us, our Fa - ther! we know Thou wilt hear · us; Nor need our
2. Love us, our Fa - ther! we know Thou wilt love · us ; We are Thy

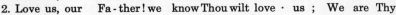

voic - es as - cend far a - way; · · Thou art a - round us, be -
chil - dren, we turn un - to Thee; · · For all a - round us, with -

side us, with - in · us: Thou wilt at - tend when we ear-nest - ly pray.
in us, a - bove us, Proofs of Thine in - fi - nite kind-ness we see.

Acknowledgments

THE EDITORS ARE UNDER DEEP OBLIGATION TO MR. E. W. NEWTON
FOR HIS VALUABLE SERVICE, WISE COUNSEL, AND ABLE LEADERSHIP

Acknowledgment is due also to Mr. Ennis D. Davis for assistance in establishing contacts with folk-song collectors in Europe and America; for the poem "A Song of Summer," from Lovejoy and Adams's *Pieces for Every Month of the Year*, published by Noble and Noble; for permission to use the poem "Pencil and Paint," from *Joan's Door* by Eleanor Farjeon, published and copyrighted 1926 by Frederick A. Stokes Company; for the poem "Snowflakes" by Mary Mapes Dodge, used by permission of Charles Scribner's Sons, owners of the copyright; for the poems "I Heard the Bells on Christmas Day" by Henry W. Longfellow and "God of the Earth, the Sky, the Sea" by Samuel Longfellow, used by permission of and by arrangement with Houghton Mifflin Company; for the poem "Moral Song," from *Songs for Parents* by John Farrar, published by the Yale University Press; for the songs "The Cowboy" and "The Roving Cowboy," reprinted from *Singing Cowboy* by Margaret Larkin, by permission of and special arrangement with Alfred A. Knopf, authorized publishers; for the tune of "The Primitive Sculptor," from *Omaha Indian Music* by Alice Cunningham Fletcher, used by permission of the Peabody Museum of Archaeology and Ethnology; for the tune on page 113 from *Jamaican Folklore*, used by permission of the American Folklore Society; for the song "The June Bug," by Victor Young, published by Schroeder and Gunther, Inc.; for the Spanish-American tunes on pages 46 and 116, used by permission of Miss Eleanor Hague and the American Folklore Society; for the tune on page 182 from *Spanish Folk Songs of New Mexico*, used by permission of Mary Van Stone, editor, and Ralph Fletcher Seymour, publisher; for the Ukrainian tune on page 41, from *Das Lied der Völker*, Volume I, used by permission of B. Schott's Söhne, Mainz, Germany; and for the Argentine tune on page 192, secured through the Pan American Union. The illustrations are by Marguerite Kaeselau.

The editors appreciate the services of Louise Krueger and Harold Rugg in arranging the integration of these songs with the other curriculum subjects.

Alphabetical Index

Alphabetical Index

PRINTED IN THE UNITED STATES OF AMERICA